SOUTH YORKSHIRE PITS

South Yorkshire Pits

Warwick Taylor

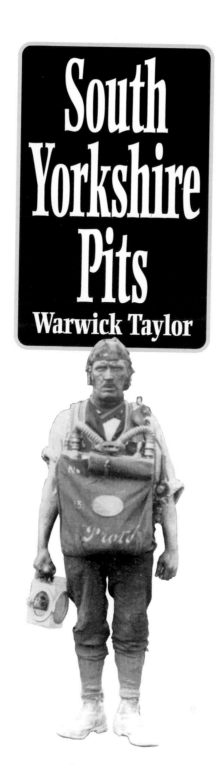

Wharncliffe Books

Dedication

To my wife Sheila, without whose love and patience I should never have been able to research and write this book, which I have dedicated in recognition of the thousands of miners past and present, and to all the Bevin Boys many of whom were conscripted to serve on the Home Front in the Yorkshire Collieries in lieu of service in the Armed Forces during the Second World War and during the period 1943-1948.

First Published in 2001
by Wharncliffe Books
Reprinted 2004
an imprint of
Pen and Sword Books Limited,
47 Church Street, Barnsley,
South Yorkshire. S70 2AS

Copyright © Warwick Taylor

For up-to-date information on other titles produced under the Wharncliffe imprint, please telephone or write to:

> **Wharncliffe Books**
> **FREEPOST**
> **47 Church Street**
> **Barnsley**
> **South Yorkshire S70 2BR**
> **Telephone (24 hours): 01226 - 734555**

ISBN: 1-903425-84-3

A CIP catalogue record of this book is available from the British Library

Cover illustration: *Front: Woolley colliery, Barnsley, 14 September 1914.*
Back: Miners Demonstration, Barnsley, 17 June 1907.

Printed in the United Kingdom by
CPI UK

CONTENTS

ACKNOWLEDGEMENTS

I would like to gratefully acknowledge the assistance of the following individuals and organizations:

Records: British Coal Corporation, British Library, Colin Jackson, Doncaster Archives and Local Studies Library, National Coal Board, National Coal Mining Museum for England, National Union of Miners, Rotherham Archives and Local Studies Library, Sheffield Archives and Local Studies Library, Wharncliffe Books.

Photographs: British Coal Corporation, National Coal Board; National Coal Mining Museum for England, National Union of Miners.

Maps: Ordnance Survey reproduced by kind permission of HM Stationery Office.

FOREWORD

From the Rt. Hon. The Lord Mason of Barnsley P.C., D.Univ, D.L.

Pits, Muckstacks and Clogs
Rarely Seen Today

In 1938 when I went underground in Wharncliffe Woodmoor 4 and 5 pit in Carlton, Barnsley, at the unbelievable age of fourteen, there were 1860 pits in England, Scotland and Wales employing 790,000 men. Today there are only twenty-five large coal mines left.

During the war years 1939-1945, 5,396 miners were killed underground. Even in peace times the industry has been riddled with disasters and thousands of lives have been lost.

Coal mining has been the most dangerous and uncivilised form of industrial employment in our country - noisy, dusty, filthy, no toilets and mice ridden. If one could have sliced the top off a coal mine and allowed the nation to see how miners toiled and sweated few would have ventured underground.

Even today old retired miners are dying of the dust disease emphysema, now recognised as an industrial disease. 100,000 miners have requests being considered, but the process is so complicated and tortuous many will die before being paid. Deaths, injuries, dust diseases, pneumoconiosis, silicosis and emphysema - what a toll of human life. During the last war the country badly needed coal to fuel war production - the Minister of Employment Ernest Bevin appealed to former miners in the Armed Forces to return to coal mining, few did. The Prime Minister, Winston Churchill held a secret meeting in the Central Hall in London to address and appeal to a gathering of miners representatives the importance of increasing coal production and the dire need of the Steel and Arms Industries - it had to be kept secret - it was indicating the real weakness of our war effort - emphasising his plea he said 'one will say, I was a fighter pilot, I was in the sub-marine service - another I marched with the Eighth Army - a fourth will say, none of you could have lived without the convoys and the Merchant Seamen' and then stressed 'you the miners in your turn will say with equal pride and with equal rights - We cut the Coal' (22 April 1943).

Yes indeed Miners have played a major part in our industrial history and gave of their best in the war and at great cost.

I do not think it has ever been fully appreciated.

Glossary

AIR CROSSING	Point where one underground roadway crosses over another to keep the airflows separate.
AIR HOSE	Flexible pipe for compressed air or water, known as bagging.
AIRWAYMAN OR WASTEMAN	Man in charge of ventilation.
ANEMOMETER	Instrument for measuring air velocity.
BANK	Top of shaft.
BANKSMAN	Man responsible for operating shaft signals.
BLACKDAMP OR STYTHE	Air contains large proportion of carbon dioxide.
BLASTING	Shotfiring.
BLUFFS	Blinkers.
BRATTICE	A temporary sheet used to divert air underground.
BUTTY	Mining contractor.
BYE-PASS	Space along haulage roadway.
CAGE	Lift in which men and materials are raised and lowered in a shaft.
CAPPEL	Device for connecting end of a rope with a cage or tub.
CAUNCHING	Ripping and dinting.
CHECK	Numbered metal disc.
CHECKWAYMAN	Man who checks the weight of coal in tubs.
CLEVIS OR CLIVVY	Safety link, used for attaching tubs to a rope.
CLIP	Device used for attaching tubs to rope on endless rope.
CLIPPER ON	Man who attaches and detaches tubs on endless rope haulage.
COAL CUTTER	Machine operated by rope haulage along coal face for cutting coal from bottom of the seam.
COAL GETTING	Extraction of coal from a seam.

COGMAN OR COGGER	Man setting chocks.
COLLIER	Coal miner.
CONTRABAND	Prohibited articles underground.
CONVEYOR	Endless belt for transporting coal or stone.
CONVEYOR-SHAKER	Method of moving material by backward and forward motion of steel troughs.
CORPORAL, DOGGY OR TURNKEEPER	Man in charge of haulage.
CREEPER	Endless chair to pull tubs uphill.
CRUMPING	Bursting due to mechanical pressure of strata.
DEPUTY	Supervisor or man in charge of a district.
DINTING	Removal of floor level to increase height.
DISTRICT	Underground area supervised by an Overman.
DOWNCAST	Shaft or drift through which air enters from the surface to ventilate mine workings.
DRIFT	Inclined roadway from surface to underground workings.
DRIVER	In charge of engine or pony.
DUCK-BILL	Mechanical loader or shaker conveyor.
DUMPLING	Wooden wedge placed between rail to prevent tubs running backwards.
FACE	Working area for extracting coal.
FARRIER	Man who shoes ponies.
FAULT	Fracture in rocks where displacement has occurred.
FILLER	Man loading coal by hand into tubs or conveyors.
FIREDAMP	Methane gas or Marsh gas.
FIRER	Man in charge of detonators and shotfiring.
FOREPOLING	Method of roof support using horizontal bars.
GANG	Term for a team of men or train of tubs.

GATE-WAY	Road leading to a longwall face.
GEARMAN	Pony driver.
GETTER	Man engaged in coal winning.
GOAF OR GOB	Area where coal has been extracted and filled with debris.
GOBBER	Man employed to pack waste into the gob.
GUMMER	Man who clears coal from dirt undercut by coal-cutting machine.
HAULAGE	Underground transport. (Direct rope haulage, endless rope haulage) over tub haulage, under tub haulage, gravity haulage, hand haulage, locomotive haulage, main and tail rope haulage and pony haulage).
HEAD FRAME OR HEAD GEAR	Steel or wooden frame at the top of the shaft which carries pulleys for hoisting rope or cable.
HEADING	Roadway driven in the coal seam.
HITCHER	Man who attaches and detaches tubs on endless rope haulage.
HURRIER OR PUTTER	Man who pushes tubs along track.
INBYE	Direction towards working place.
JIGGER	Another term for shake conveyor.
KEEKER	Foreman in charge of surface screening plant.
LAGGING	Wood or steel placed behind arches or girders to protect roadway from falling rock.
LAMP-MAN	Man in charge of the lamp room.
LAMP-ROOM	Room where miners' lamps are kept.
LASHING	Attaching tubs to endless rope haulage by means of chains.
LIFTING	Raising the floor level in a mine.
LOADER	Mechanical shovel for loading tubs.
LONG WALL	Coal face not exceeding 250 yards.

Mine or Pit	Underground workings for extraction of mined materials.
Miner	Man working in a mine.
Muck	Stone or dirt obtained from ripping and dinting.
Nog	Wood or steel wedge used to give support to coal after undercutting.
Onsetter	Man in charge of cage at pit bottom.
Out-bye	The direction away from the coalface.
Overman	Underground under-manager.
Pack	Stonewalls to support roof of mine workings.
Packer	Man engaged in setting of stone walls.
Paddy Mail	Underground transport for men.
Picksman	Man who gets coal by hand.
Pillar and Stall or Bord and Pillar	Mining coal by means of a series of stalls, leaving pillars of coal to act as roof supports.
Pneumoconiosis	Dust disease of the lungs.
Pony Driver or Pony Putter	Man in charge of a pony during its work.
Prop	Wooden or steel support used for supporting roof. (Anchor prop, catch prop, cut prop, holing prop, safety prop, stake prop, steel prop, sunk prop or watch prop).
Putter	A man who pushes tubs.
Putting	Movement of tubs along rail track.
Rerailer	Device for putting derailed tubs back on track.
Ripping	Removal of roof space to provide adequate roadway.
Road or Roadway	Underground passage.
Runaway	Loose tubs caused by break in attached rope.

SAFETY LAMP | Miner's oil or electric lamp used for illumination and detecting gas.

SCREENS | The plant on the surface where coal is graded into sizes.

SEAM | A flat deposit of coal or other mineral.

SHAFT | Vertical passageway from surface to underground for the raising and lowering of men and materials, as well as for ventilation.

SIGNALS | A series of bell code signals used in direct rope haulage, gravity haulage, endless rope haulage and mail and tail haulage.

SILICOSIS | Dust disease of the lungs.

SINKING | Excavation for a shaft.

SKIP | Large container for hoisting coal up a shaft.

SNAP OR SNAP TIME | Small meal break.

STALL | Room in Pillar and Stall system.

STALLMAN | Miner working in a stall.

STINT | Allocated working area for each miner during a shift.

STONE DUSTING | Spreading of fine stone dust in roadways to reduce amount of inflammable dust.

STOWER | Man engaged in stowing work.

STRATA | Seams or beds.

STRIPPING | Clearance of coal from the face after shot-firing.

SUBSIDENCE | Settling of strata due to underground excavation.

SURVEYOR | Official who surveys underground workings.

SYLVESTER | A device for withdrawing props.

TIMBERMAN | Man who sets supports.

TIP | Heap of waste material raised from a coal mine.

TIPPLER | Mechanical cylinder used for turning over tubs.

TUB, TRAM, CORVE OR MINE CAR | A wagon used for transporting coal.

TUNNEL	Passage or Roadway underground.
TUNNELLER	Man engaged in driving a tunnel.
UPCAST	The shaft through which air returns to the surface.
VENTILATION	Circulation of air in mine workings.
WARWICK OR DERRICK	Safety device attached to tubs to prevent them from running backwards on inclines.
WASTE	Part of the goaf between packs, where the roof caves in.
WEIGHMAN	Man in charge of the weighbridge.
WHITEDAMP	Air mixed with high percentage of carbon monoxide.
WINDING	Hoisting a cage up a shaft or tub up an incline.
WINNING	The getting and loading of coal.
WORKINGS	The area of a seam where coal is mined.
WRINGER OR RINGER	A steel bar used for breaking coal.
WROUGHT OUT OR WORKED OUT	An area from which coal has been extracted, sometimes referred to as exhausted.
YARD	Unit of length of three feet (91.44 cms).

INTRODUCTION

The last 150 years have without question been the most tumultuous in the industrial history of South Yorkshire, at the heart of which has always been the mining industry and its numerous supporting industries.

Yorkshire is the largest county in England and positioned over numerous coal seams, the richest of which lies beneath the area contained in lines drawn between Leeds, Huddersfield, Sheffield and Doncaster. Barnsley is roughly in the centre.

The chief beneficiaries from the discovery of, and subsequent rapid increase in demand for coal as the industrial revolution progressed, were the established landowning families. They found themselves in possession of vast coal deposits, for which there appeared to be an unlimited demand. The revenue from satisfying this demand enabled them to invest further in the essential railway and canal communications system, which in turn generated further revenue. This resulted in their becoming ever more involved in local and national politics and to follow a lifestyle utterly different from that of their workers.

Of the workers, no more than seventy per cent were local people, the balance being drawn from many different parts of England, Ireland and particularly Wales, and in many cases entire families would be employed in some element of pit work.

The working day usually began at four in the morning with the 'knocker up' tapping on the bedroom window with a wire atop a long pole. Breakfast was still a thing of the future, however a 'snap tin', containing bread and jam sandwiches, occasionally accompanied with a piece of cheese and always a bottle of water. The chink of snap tin on bottle, was the rhythmic accompaniment to the clatter of clogs as the miners set off in the early morning towards the pit head.

In the early days, there were no 'perks' for the miners. Even the coal which they had hewn themselves still had to be paid for when delivered to their homes, a ton at a time, and shovelled into the coal hole positioned at the front of each of their homes. These houses normally consisted of a two-up-two-down terraced cottage, usually the property of the colliery owner, rented out to the miner. An outside toilet and cold running water were also the norm, all hot water being boiled in a pan or kettle on the fire.

Before the introduction of pithead baths it was usual for a miner to bathe in a tin bath in front of the fire. A scene which is conjured up in all of our minds' eyes is the image of the exhausted miner, assisted by his wife, washing off the grime of many hours of grinding toil in the bowels of the earth.

The leisure pursuits of miners have always included fishing, gardening and pigeon racing of various kinds. The most common games of chance were pitch-and-toss and nipsy, while children played such team games as rounders, football and individual games such as hoops and whip-and-top.

'Feast week' was the annual break from the pit and escape to the newly developing seaside resorts on the Yorkshire and Lancashire coasts to which specially chartered trains and charabancs took entire communities on holiday.

Contrary to popular belief, the period of the industrial revolution was not one of steady growth and development, but was wracked with uncertainty and financial upheaval, often aggravated by the poverty of the working classes, the coming of trade unions and strikes in protest at often appalling working conditions.

By 1842, women of any age and children under the age of ten were no longer permitted to work underground. In 1900, the age limit for children working underground was again raised, this time to thirteen. It is interesting to note that there was considerable resistance among the workers to these changes, which had the effect of putting many mining families in financial difficulty by seriously reducing, or even stopping the income of women and children.

Working conditions in the mining industry have always been hard and often dangerous, with long hours and, certainly in the earlier years, little reward. Few underground workers lived to enjoy any form of retirement, often being killed by industrial disease or in accidents.

Some mine owners did show a surprising degree of moral responsibility for their workers, providing education and religious guidance, medical care and housing. All of these elements, of course, bred loyalty from their workers, but also made any form of resistance from them extremely difficult. Imagine the dilemma of the miners and their families when pressed by trade union representatives to strike for improved pay and conditions on the one hand and the threat of eviction and the withdrawal of the various concessions offered by the mine owner on the other.

While this book contains many statistics covering the histories of the larger and better known pits, their owners and developers, an attempt has also been made to put flesh on the bones of those who built and sustained the coal industry of South Yorkshire, at one time the largest industrial complex in Europe.

At the turn of the twentieth century, Yorkshire had almost 450 pits, but by 1945 this number was reduced by half.

All the pits included here were among those taken over by the National Coal Board on 1 January 1947.

The years 1910, 1927, 1945 and 1972 have been randomly selected to illustrate the variations of surface and underground manpower and coal seams statistics at various stages in recent coal mining history.

While every effort has been made to include all collieries in South Yorkshire, records of a few of the less well known pits have not survived and have therefore been omitted.

CHAPTER ONE

Commission on Employment of Women and Children in Mines

Women and Children in Mines

In the early days children formed a significant proportion of the colliery labour force with 30 per cent being under the age of twenty, sub-divided into proportions of 0.5 per cent between five and nine, 12.5 per cent between ten and fourteen and 17 per cent between fifteen and nineteen years of age.

Thin seam pits with roadways too low for ponies and men to move tubs of coal were considered too expensive to raise. It was cheaper to employ child labour. In some cases mothers took babies with them underground.

A collier's wage during the middle of the nineteenth century was twenty to twenty-five shillings [£1-£1.25] per week. Hurriers would receive five shillings [25p] per week at the age of eleven and twelve shillings [60p] per week at age seventeen. Trappers, on the other hand, earned a daily wage of sixpence [2¹/₂p].

Candles and tools used at work were paid for out of the workers' wages and not by the pit owners.

Most children worked for a collier and were paid by him, yet few ever received any payment. Wages went straight to their fathers, who considered feeding and clothing was sufficient to their needs. The most important factor of all was the moral danger to both sexes working together in an unhealthy environment.

'*Trapper*'. Children's Employment Commission, 1842.

'Hurrier'. Children's Employment Commission, 1842.

On 20 October 1840, a Children's Employment Commission was set up to conduct an enquiry into the employment of children in mines, factories and workshops. Six sub-commissioners were appointed in November of that year to carry out the task.

Jelinger Cookson Symons was assigned to the Yorkshire area in order to interview mine owners, managers, miners, doctors, clergymen, young children and numerous individual witnesses connected in one way or another with the collieries.

Samuel Scriven, another of the six sub-commissioners, was originally assigned to North Staffordshire but later transferred to West Yorkshire to provide assistance for Symons to cover the large number of pits in Yorkshire.

Two commissioners, together with Symons and Scriven, went underground at coal mines in Barnsley, Flockton, Halifax and Elland. Scriven particularly wanted to question children in their working environment.

It soon became apparent that reformers who pressed for these commissions were concerned about the physical and spiritual welfare of the children, whereas mine owners often claimed to be unaware of children being employed at very young ages. Parents, on the other hand, condoned child employment in the mines as they would command the lowest of wages from their employers and provide an additional source of income for the parents.

However, the results of the enquiries the sub-commissioners made were varied in as much that it became obvious that many children underplayed the real truth in their statements. They had no doubt been well briefed by their parents about their answers to questions for fear they may lose their employment.

A typical working day would start with breakfast, consisting of bread, milk or porridge, before setting off for a five or six o'clock start at the pit. Lunch would consist of bread, sometimes with meat or cheese, depending upon whether or not a household could afford such luxuries out of a meagre income. Meal breaks were never standardised but were fitted in where possible and rarely exceeded fifteen minutes.

Boys and girls were used without discrimination, undertaking jobs that were hard and dangerous although, exceptionally, the Earl Fitzwilliam collieries and Newton Chambers colliery at Thorncliffe did not allow the employment of female labour. Many children started work underground at the early age of five years and were normally employed as trappers. This job involved sitting in a small recess and being responsible for the opening and closing of trap doors through which tubs (or 'corves', sing. 'corf') would pass en-route from the coal face with full loads and return empty. The corves varied in size and were capable of carrying up to half a ton of coal. It was essential that the trappers kept the trap doors open once a corf had passed in order not to impede the flow of fresh air to the areas where it was needed. Stale or stagnant air, when combined with methane gas, can quickly form an explosive mixture so adequate ventilation was essential in order to prevent this from happening. These young trappers seldom had candles and remained in total darkness for between ten and eleven hours a day, six days a week - a frightening and terrifying experience for anyone, let alone a five-year old.

Older children up to fifteen years of age were employed as horse drivers, jenny boys and hurriers.

Horse driving was the best occupation for children involving little heavy work. The Earl Fitzwilliam pits, exceptionally, employed twenty-one horse drivers together with an equal number of assistants. Jenny boys were required in areas where a pulley system was attached to corves for descending on a steep incline to a lower level, by which the speed of descent was controlled by a brake operated by a Jenny boy. Symons discovered a large number of these boys at Elsecar collieries.

Colliers working at the coal face would hew the coal and then shovel it onto a riddle or sieve which was held by the hurrier who would then separate the small coal and throw the larger pieces into the corf. When it was full a mark would be made to show which collier had cut the coal, after which the hurrier would then pull the corf from the coal face to the pit bottom where horses were used. Pulling a corf would, in most cases, involve the use of a rope or chain, one end being attached to the corf and the other to a belt worn round the waist. In some cases the hurrier would need the assistance of a thruster, a young child to push the back of the corf.

Hurriers were employed directly by the miners or coal getters who were therefore in the unique position of employing members of their own family.

Symons calculated that on average the hurriers had to push a loaded corf a distance of 150 yards from the coal faces to the horse gate and back again twenty times during a shift, covering a distance of three and a half miles. Pits at Worsbrough involved distances in excess of nine miles.

In his report of July 1841, Symons described in detail the appalling conditions in which these children had to work from the early age of five years although the normal age was seven or eight years. The work often caused deformity, stunted growth, crippled gait and a variety of diseases resulting in premature old age and death. Death and injury were commonplace. Many accidents were caused by ascending and descending in corves hooked to ropes which collided against the sides of the shaft, thus dislodging the occupants who fell to their deaths on the pit bottom.

Roof falls, explosions caused by firedamp, the breaking of ropes and chains and injury from runaway corves were daily hazards. Some children worked all day in water and mud, which, due to the lack of sanitation, was more than likely to be highly polluted. The statement given by the fifteen-year old hurrier, Fanny Drake (page 22), suggests this. Children became too tired to eat after a day's work. Furthermore, there was evidence of considerable child abuse whereby miners employing their own children, forced them to work longer hours to make up for any time lost during the day.

Swearing and indecent language was widely prevalent.

There were cases involving 'bastardy' in the pits in which men were forced to marry girls they had seduced.

Symons concluded that children were obviously totally ignorant of any other way of life. Conversely, seeing children running about and playing when they came up from the pit, might create a false impression that they were happy with their environment. This was the view taken by George Traviss, a Barnsley coal owner.

The Bill laid before Parliament had three readings in which the criticism was voiced that by excluding women from the mines was likely to cause distress and financial hardship to families. The publication of the report in June 1842 caused a public outcry. Newspapers referred to the employment of women and children as 'slavery', which had been abolished nine years earlier.

However it was initially felt that Lord Ashley would propose that no children under the age of eighteen years should be allowed to work underground, causing coal owners to fear a demand for higher wages and improved working conditions. Opposition in the House of Lords forced some changes to the Bill.

The Act was finally passed on 4 August 1842, which ruled that from 1 March 1843, it became illegal to employ a woman or girl of any age or boys under the age of ten to work underground at a mine or colliery in Britain. However, despite fines of not less than £5 and not more than £10 for not complying with the Act, the period of adjustment was far longer because only one Commissioner of Mines was appointed to cover the whole of Britain to check on its implementation. The result was that women continued to work illegally and coal owners continued to turn a blind eye.

The numbers of children working in the mines increased as the work force increased but pit owners seemed to stick to the 'over ten years of age' rule for the employment of young boys. This changed dramatically in 1872 when the *Mines Regulation Act* increased the boys' minimum age limit to twelve.

In 1990, the *Sex Discrimination Act,* made it possible once again for women to work underground, albeit under entirely different working conditions and standards compared to that of almost 150 years ago.

'Thruster' - pushing with the head. Children's Employment Commission, 1842.

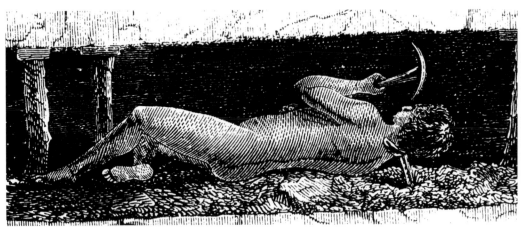

'Hewer' - working naked. Children's Employment Commission, 1842.

I went to pit myself when I was five years old and two of my daughters go. It does them no harm. It never did me none.
Mrs Mary Ann Watson of Flockton.

I have had to hurry up to the calves of my legs in water. It was as bad as this a fortnight at a time.. .my feet were skinned, and just as if they were scalded, for the water was bad: it had stood sometime; and I was off work owing to it, and had a headache and bleeding at my nose.
Fanny Drake, aged fifteen, hurrier.

I work now as a banksman; I have three sons living, one of them went into the pit with me when he was three years old, and commenced working regularly as a hurrier when he was between five and six; that was at Flockton; another began between four and five; another between five and six.
Joseph Gledhill, aged forty-eight years, banksman.

I stand and open and shut the door; I'm generally in the dark, and sit me down against the door.. .I never see daylight now, except on Sundays.
John Saville, aged seven years.

I'm a trapper in the Gawber pit. It does not tire me, but I have to trap without a light and I'm scared. I go at four and sometimes half past three in the morning, and come out at five and half past. I never go to sleep. Sometimes I sing when I've light, but not in the dark; I dare not sing then. I don't like being in the pit.
Sarah Gooder, aged eight years.

I am not paid wages myself; the man who employs me pays my father; but I don't know how much it is.
Elizabeth Day, aged seventeen years.

I push with my head sometimes; it makes my head sore sometimes, so that I cannot bear it touched; it is soft too.
Fanny Drake aged fifteen years, hurrier.

It is harder work than we ought to do a deal. I have been lamed in my ankle, and strained in my back.
Elizabeth Day, aged seventeen years.

I have to go up to the headings with the men; they are all naked there; I am got well used to that, and don't care now much about it.
Mary Barrett, aged fourteen years.

Girls regularly perform all the various offices of trapping, hurrying, filling, riddling, tipping and occasionally getting. The springs which ooze through the best cased shafts, trickle down its sides, and keep up a perpetual drizzle below. The chamber or area at the bottom of the shaft is almost always sloppy and muddy, and the escape from it consists of a labyrinth of black passages, often not above four feet square. In great numbers of the coal-pits in this district the men work in a state of perfect nakedness, and are in this state assisted in their labour by females of all ages, from girls of six years old to women of twenty-one, these females being themselves quite naked down to the waist. Assembled round a fire a group of men, boys and girls, some of whom were of the age of puberty, the girls as well as the boys stark naked down to the waist, their hair bound up with a tight cap, and trousers supported by their hips. Their sex was only recognisable by their breasts, and some little difficulty occasionally arose in pointing out to me which were girls and which were boys, and which caused a good deal of laughing and joking.
Jelinger Cookson Symons.

One of the most disgusting sights I have ever seen was that of young females, dressed like boys in trousers, crawling on all fours, with belts round their waists and chains passing between their legs. Chained, belted, harnessed, like dogs in a go-cart, black, saturated with wet, and more than half naked, crawling upon their hands and feet, and dragging their heavy loads behind them, they present an appearance indescribably disgusting and unnatural.
Samuel Scrivens.

The getter I work with wears a flannel waistcoat when he is poorly,

but when he is quite well he wears nothing at all.
Fanny Drake, aged fifteen years, hurrier.

The work is far too hard for me, the sweat runs off me all over. I'm very tired at night. Sometimes when we get home at night we have no power to wash us, and then we go to bed. Sometimes we fall asleep in the chair. Father said last night it was both a shame and a disgrace to work as we do, but there was nought else for us to do.
Ann Eggley, Gawber Pit.

Mark the effect of the system on women: it causes a total ignorance of all domestic duties; they know nothing that they ought to know; they are rendered unfit for the duties of women by overwork. They are wholly disqualified from even learning how to discharge the duties of wife and mother. The evidence of the work people themselves is worth more than all the rest, for they know what they suffer, and what the consequences are.
Extracts from speech by Lord Ashley, 7 June 1842.

CHAPTER TWO

John Brown & Company Ltd

John Brown established his own business in 1837 after borrowing £500 from the Sheffield Banking Company. It soon became the leading manufacturer of iron and steel at the Atlas Steel and Iron Works, which had been established in 1856 in Sheffield. It supplied collieries with headgear and other essential mining equipment and employed 4,500 workers.

The company, realising the potential to grasp business opportunities in the fast growing colliery and railway industries, decided to invest in the coal business in 1873, acquired Aldwarke Main and Car House collieries in Rotherham and sank a new Rotherham Main colliery at Canklow in 1891.

By 1900 the combined output of these collieries was over 6,000 tons per day. In addition the company acquired share capital in the Dalton Main collieries, which owned pits at Roundwood and Silverwood.

By 1914 the John Brown Company had become one of the largest coal producers in South Yorkshire with an annual output of two and a half million tons.

Engraving of John Brown's Atlas Steel and Iron Works, Sheffield.

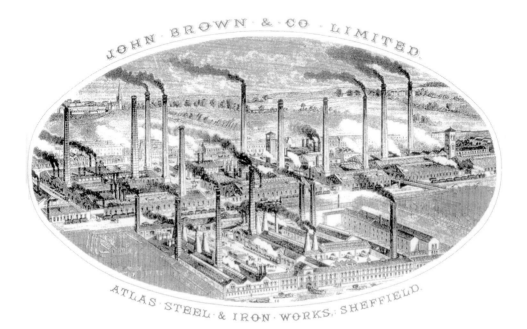

The company was not, however, without competition as a newly formed group, the United Steel Company, formed in 1918, had bought Rothervale Colliery Company. Rothervale had been incorporated in 1875 to acquire properties of the Fence Colliery Company, which at that time comprised of the Fence and Orgreave Collieries. This new company immediately established Treeton Colliery but was having major fault displacement problems in both shafts at Thurcroft Main Colliery at the same time.

Towards the end of the first decade of the 1900s the Brown Company had joined forces with the Sheepbridge Coal and Iron Company in order to sink and develop Rossington Colliery. Sheepbridge was also associated with other collieries at Tinsley Park, Dinnington and Maltby, while John Brown and Company was associated with the collieries at Maltby and Cortonwood.

It is likely that the appearance of United Steel on the coal scene, probably prevented further expansion of coal interests for the Brown Empire. Certainly their main concerns were iron and steel. They were well known for their improvements to the Bessemer process, a method of making steel by blasting compressed air through molten iron to burn out excess carbon and other impurities. In 1848 the invention by Brown of conical steel spring buffers for railway carriages and wagons brought more employment for the factory.

Private ownership, John Brown & Co. Ltd, standard gauge coal wagon.

Rotherham Main Colliery, note the John Brown & Co. coal wagons.

Craven's Railway Carriage and Wagon Company became a subsidiary of the John Brown group producing many standard gauge railway wagons for transporting coal during the 1920s.

John Brown's, however, became best known for the manufacture of armour plating for British Naval ships.

In 1899 John Brown and Company purchased the Clydebank Engineering Company, manufacturers of the famous Cunard Liners.

Aldwarke Main and Rotherham Main Collieries remained as part of the company until nationalisation in 1947.

CHAPTER THREE

The Dearne and Dove Canal

Plans for the Dearne and Dove Canal were agreed by Acts of Parliament in June 1793. It was to run from Swinton through Wath-upon-Dearne and Wombwell and join up with the Barnsley Canal at Hoyle Mill. Two branches were to be built, one to Elsecar of just over two miles and another of the same length to Worsbrough. The project would involve constructing nineteen locks on the main canal raising the level by 127 feet from the River Don, with the addition of six locks on the Elsecar branch bringing the level up to forty-eight feet. Two reservoirs were planned at Elsecar and Worsbrough and a 472 yards tunnel at Adwick on Dearne.

The canal was ready for use in December 1798 at Elsecar and the transportation of coal from the colliery started immediately. However, in 1804 the stop lock leading to the Barnsley Canal was flooded and the Dearne and Dove officially opened and able to accommodate boats of fifty-eight feet in length.

The Barnsley Canal up until now was acquiring the coal trade but when the Dearne and Dove became operational, half the tonnage shipped from Barnsley Basin, terminus of the Barnsley Canal, transferred to the new route.

Dearne and Dove canal at Stairfoot. Barnsley Coal Board.

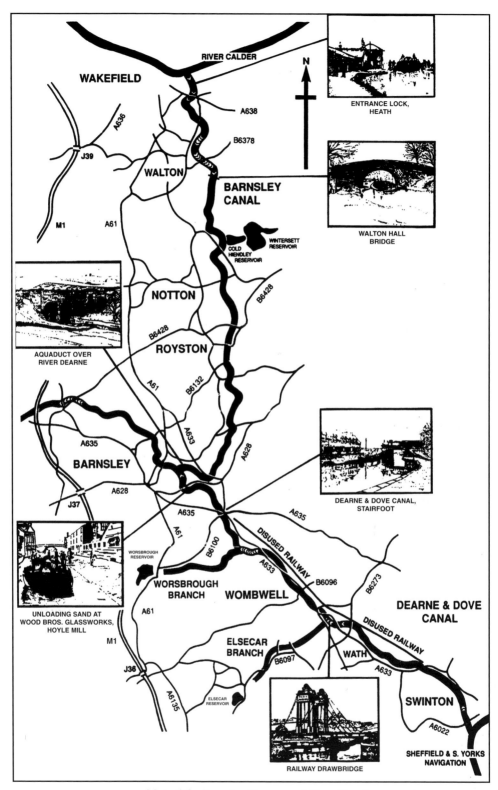

ENTRANCE LOCK,
HEATH

WALTON HALL
BRIDGE

AQUADUCT OVER
RIVER DEARNE

DEARNE & DOVE CANAL,
STAIRFOOT

UNLOADING SAND AT
WOOD BROS. GLASSWORKS,
HOYLE MILL

RAILWAY DRAWBRIDGE

RIVER CALDER

WAKEFIELD

WALTON

BARNSLEY
CANAL

NOTTON

ROYSTON

BARNSLEY

WORSBROUGH
BRANCH

WOMBWELL

ELSECAR
BRANCH

WATH

SWINTON

DEARNE & DOVE
CANAL

SHEFFIELD & S. YORKS
NAVIGATION

WINTERSETT
RESERVOIR

COLD
HIENDLEY
RESERVOIR

WORSBROUGH
RESERVOIR

ELSECAR
RESERVOIR

DISUSED RAILWAY

DISUSED RAILWAY

Map of the Barnsley, Dearne and Dove Canal.

The Dearne and Dove Canal at Wath, 1949. Barnsley Coal Board.

Problems were encountered with water shortages supplying Barnsley from the Worsbrough reservoir due to droughts in 1804 and 1805. In 1810 as many as 2,334 boats were using the canal and in 1826 the depth of the reservoir was increased by four and a half feet.

The traffic using the Dearne and Dove Canal proved it to be a prosperous venture and by 1928 150,000 tons, mainly coal, had been transported.

Coal barges at Manvers Main Colliery, c.1910.

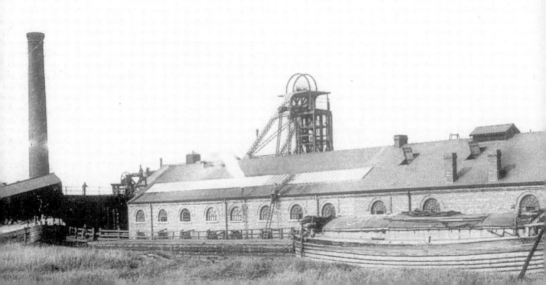

Railway drawbridge at Brampton, 1949. Barnsley Coal Board.

However in 1840 the North Midland Railway opened, posing a threat to the canal traffic, and the Don Navigation took over the Dearne and Dove in 1846.

The canal continued to serve the coalfields of the Barnsley area to make the waterway viable in the face of railway competition.

In 1889 an operating company, the Sheffield and South Yorkshire Navigation, was set up to manage all four of the South Yorkshire canals, the Sheffield Canal, the Don Navigation, the Stainforth and Keadby and the Dearne and Dove.

In 1906 problems developed with the Worsbrough Branch due to subsidence from nearby colliery workings which, despite costly repairs, led to its closure.

By 1928 the Elsecar Branch had experienced similar problems and in 1934 the last boat made the passage to Barnsley. The Dearne and Dove was now closed except for a short section at either end.

By 1942 the Barnsley Canal had closed and traffic on the Dearne and Dove from Manvers Main colliery at Wath to the Don ceased.

Thus the canals declined, but in 1984 a newly formed Barnsley Canal Group took over the task of restoration.

The Worsbrough basin had already been restored along a short length of canal which is fed from the reservoir and has an overflow into the River Dove.

The Elsecar Branch, with its six locks, presents little difficulty and full restoration commenced in 1991. The Elsecar Project plans to establish an industrial and social museum in the original Earl Fitzwilliam workshops adjacent to the canal basin.

CHAPTER FOUR

Earl Fitzwilliam

Earl Fitzwilliam of Wentworth Woodhouse, was a wealthy landowner involved in numerous enterprises including Elsecar Pits and Iron Furnaces. He had his own internal railway system and link to the canal system, giving his enterprises direct access to the wider national markets. Among his other interests, Earl Fitzwilliam was chairman of the Dearne and Dove Canal Company, which in 1798 opened a two mile branch canal linking Elsecar and Brampton.

During the first half of the nineteenth century annual coal sales increased from 70,000 to over 300,000 tons, which of course gave rise to a considerable increase in the number of pits sunk and of people employed in the industry.

The Fitzwilliam family took the view that the poor and less fortunate members of the population were the responsibility of the upper classes, in particular in respect of their religious and moral guidance. This view resulted in a management/worker relationship which was quite revolutionary in a time when the majority of mine owners totally disregarded the welfare of their work forces. They

Wentworth Woodhouse, home of Earl Fitzwilliam.

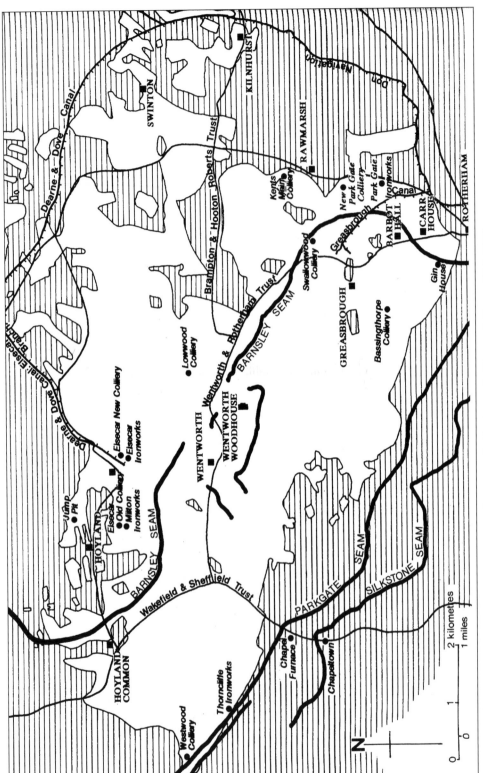

Map of canals, coal seams and collieries on the Wentworth Estate 1740–1840.

Wentworth Woodhouse, home of Earl Fitzwilliam, under military protection during the 1893 strike.

were regarded as only one step removed from beasts of burden and as such, to be dispensed with once they ceased to produce wealth for their employers.

However, the Fitzwilliams had rows of good quality stone cottages built adjacent to the colliery to house their workers and, although rent free housing for miners and their families was not uncommon, the standard of accommodation was, to say the least, basic. The miners' homes at Fitzwilliam's Elsecar pit were of a superior quality and larger than usual, consisting of four rooms, a pantry, a small back yard with an ash pit, a shared toilet between every six houses and a pig sty, with a small garden nearby. The small space to the front of each house was walled and kept neat with flagstones and flower borders. A low gate was fitted to prevent young children straying onto the road. The weekly rent for these houses and their gardens was two shillings (10p) per week.

In addition to housing, the local Mechanics Institute, library and schools were all either provided or supported by the Fitzwilliams. In the case of the schools, fees were levied for the education of the children at rates varying between two and eight pence [1p to 4p] per

Miners houses, Newstead Avenue, Fitzwilliam.

week. A fee which some families would consider excessive when every penny was so hard won to make a living wage for the household.

In the event of an employee's death, his widow was granted a weekly pension of two shillings and six pence [13p], although after the death of the 5th Earl this system was reviewed with an increase up to seven shillings and sixpence [37^1/$_2$p]. On retirement an employee would receive an allowance, although many worked until they were either too old or infirm, and records show that a John Burgan worked until he was ninety-three. Similarly a Thomas Wainwright was granted an allowance of twelve shillings [60p] a week in 1828 at the age of ninety-one when Law Wood Colliery closed. These are, of course, exceptional cases as the majority died within two years of retirement. The most common cause of death was emphysema, the legacy of a lifetime of inhaling coal and stone dust.

Support in the form of sick benefit, irrespective of the number of weeks absent from work, was another benefit of Fitzwilliam employment. Works' fêtes, Christmas boxes and food hand-outs were all part of a unique welfare scheme which cost the Fitzwilliams £150,000 in 1840 alone. The benefits to the Fitzwilliams were of course a high level of loyalty from their workers and freedom from the growing militancy of the working classes as a whole and miners in particular.

Pit safety was another serious aspect for consideration, generally regarded as an occupational hazard of little concern in other collieries. Joshua and Benjamin Biram, father and son, were local managers and mining engineers who worked for Fitzwilliam, and were well known for introducing several inventions which included a ventilating fan installed at Elsecar, an anemometer and a safety lamp, Such was their dedication to the safety of the miners that on 27 October 1856 a silver cup costing £20 was bought by the workers of the Elsecar collieries and presented to Benjamin as a token of the high esteem in which he was held, and for his kindness and consideration towards them. Though only marginally health and safety conscious by today's standards, the successful inventions pioneered by the Birams certainly made mining a safer undertaking.

If an employee was dismissed he had the right of appeal to Earl Fitzwilliam, which usually resulted in reinstatement. However, membership of a trade union was an 'offence' which the Fitzwilliams were not prepared to tolerate. At a large meeting of colliers at Hood Hill, three miles from Elsecar, 4,000 miners were being persuaded by speakers not to earn more than two shillings and sixpence [13p] a day. The restriction of earnings and an eight hour working day which had already been adopted by the South Yorkshire Miners Association to bring pressure on the coal owners no doubt put many of the Fitzwilliam workers into a dilemma.

Shortly afterwards, no doubt as a result of this meeting, the Association had spread its influence to the Fitzwilliam pits, resulting in his Lordship's sharp and uncompromising reaction. He expected his employees to be totally loyal. He immediately issued an order in April 1844 that all colliers joining the Association were to leave their work and houses. This resulted in the closing down of the pits at Elsecar and Park Gate. He dismissed men who continued to defy him. Two days later he received an undertaking from the men renouncing all connections with the Association, whereupon Fitzwilliam ordered the collieries to be reopened, thus reverting to the rights and duties of the master/servant relationship.

Although the miners may have thought at the time that wages would be raised and conditions improved by joining an association or union, it would have in no way compensated them for the loss of privileges they already enjoyed, which certainly was not the case in other Yorkshire collieries.

What need therefore of an association or union? To the Earl this was an unnecessary attempt at combination, and he was shocked by their ingratitude. Surely, his provision for their employees and families in sickness, unemployment, retirement and death could not equal the doubtful benefits of association or union membership.

The Fitzwilliams had a good mine safety record with only one major disaster at Elsecar pit, in December 1852, when ten miners were killed as a result of an explosion caused by ignition of firedamp.

Fitzwilliam Collieries and Numbers of Miners Employed 1795 - 1856

1795	Elsecar, 'Old' & 'New', Lawwood, Westwood	79
1819	Elsecar, 'Old' & 'New', Haugh, Lawwood, Brampton	197
1828	Elsecar, 'Old' & 'New', Lawwood, Rainber Park, Swallowwood, Park Gate	317
1845	Elsecar, 'High', 'Middle' & 'Low' (Hemingfield) Strafford Main, Park Gate, Kents Main.	587
1856	Elsecar Collieries, Park Gate Collieries, Strafford Main	869

The Fitzwilliam line 1815 - 1979

William Thomas Spencer Wentworth Fitzwilliam KG, DCL, DL. 6th Earl 1815-1902.

William Charles de Meuron Wentworth Fitzwilliam KCVO, CBE, DSO, JP, DL. 7th Earl 1872-1943.

William Henry Lawrence Peter Wentworth Fitzwilliam DSC. 8th Earl 1910-1948.

Eric Spencer Wentworth Fitzwilliam. 9th Earl 1883-1952.

William Thomas George Wentworth Fitzwilliam TD, JP, DL, OBE. 10th Earl 1904-1979.

No Heir.

The company continued to trade as The Earl Fitzwilliam Collieries Company until nationalisation in 1947.

Copy of letter to the Home Secretary:

21 January 1870

Sir,

At the earliest possible moment after my last communication with you, a meeting of Magistrates was held at Barnsley, to take into consideration the best mode of dealing with the lawless portion of the population in the neighbourhood of Thorncliffe.

It was decided at that meeting to order an addition of 15 men to be made to the police force of this (the West) Riding of Yorkshire. I am however informed by Captain McNeill, the Chief Constable of the

Riding, that upon laying this resolution of the Magistrates assembled at Barnsley before Police Committee, the West Riding solicitor advised that the addition of 15 men to the force, even temporarily cannot take place without an order of sessions.

The difficulty of carrying out your suggestion as to the employment of Special Constables, is very great, as I must not conceal from you that among the class from which the bulk of the Special Constables would be drawn, there exists considerable sympathy with the Unionists, consequently with the rioters.

From the fact of the rioters being chiefly resident in the neighbourhood, it is necessary that the protection afforded to Messrs Newton Chambers & Co. should be continuous as it is impossible to foresee at what moment disturbances may occur.

It is obvious that even if the bulk of the population did not sympathise with the rioters, they could not leave their homes and regular occupations for the length of time necessary to render effectual protection to those whose lives and properties are endangered.

I regret to add that my anticipation as to renewed disturbances have proved too well founded: an outbreak of a far more serious character having occurred this morning; I am informed that the police were overpowered, and a range of new houses completely wrecked; under these considerations I have requested the Magistrates to take measures for providing accommodation for troops, should it prove necessary to call on the military for assistance.

Yours faithfully,

signed Fitzwilliam

CHAPTER FIVE

The Fountain and Burnley Partnership

During the 1890s Woolley and North Gawber Collieries were in financial difficulties. Woolley was owned by the Woolley Coal Company of 1867 and North Gawber, the property of Fountain and Burnley since 1882, was used as a security to the bank in respect of the partners' overdraft which was in excess of £14,000.

George John Burnley, junior partner and manager at North Gawber, no doubt influenced the purchase of the ailing Woolley, but unfortunately he died in 1894, only a few months after the agreement to purchase Woolley was made.

The new company was headed by Joseph Fountain, an experienced colliery proprietor who came from a family involved in large colliery interests since the 1830s. Other members of the family, who formed partnerships with North Gawber Colliery were the brothers, Joseph, Henry and George Fountain, together with their sister's husband G J Burnley. His father, John Burnley, took an interest in his colliers and was jointly responsible with John Marsden, the senior colliery partner, for establishing Woolley Colliery School.

G J was a mining engineer and gained his colliery experience before he became owner of North Gawber. He continued as manager and eventually became a partner. He died in 1894 at the age of forty-six.

By late 1894 Joseph Fountain, the sole male survivor of his generation, together with his sister Ellen, the widow of George John Burnley, were the owners of North Gawber Colliery, while Joseph Fountain owned Darton Colliery, as well as being a partner at Haigh Colliery.

Prior to Burnley's death an agreement had been signed to purchase Woolley Colliery for the sum of £22,377, but due to family financial problems, the purchase was delayed for two years until 1896 when North Gawber and Woolley Collieries became amalgamated into the new private company of Fountain and Burnley Limited for the sum of £47,000. This merger provided sufficient capital to pay off a substantial part of the outstanding debts to the banks.

The new company held its first meeting in June 1896 with Joseph Fountain, chairman of directors and colliery owner, as the major shareholder.

The shareholders were:

H S Childe	director and mining engineer
H B Nash	managing director
C H Moss	director and accountant
J Hewitt	director and lawyer
W H Copley	secretary and accountant
Wakefield and Barnsley Union Bank Ltd	colliery bankers for Woolley
Elizabeth Brook and Herbert Pearson	previously Woolley owners.
Barnsley Banking Co. Ltd	colliery bankers for North Gawber

Total share value at £10 each, £9,380.

Debentures were issued to G H Wentworth, land and mineral owner, Elizabeth Brook and Herbert Pearson, Charles Methley (a previous Woolley owner) and H B Nash amounting to £41,600 making an initial total capital of £50,980.

The collieries at Swallow Hill, Darton, which was Joseph Fountain's own property, and Haigh remained separate under the management of George Fountain and Sons.

The new company was quite financially modest in size, with a high proportion of debenture capital, but it was not until 1902 that a dividend of 14 per cent was declared. It rose to 40 per cent in 1907 but fluctuated in the next few years with dividends dropping as low as 10 per cent before rising to 30 per cent in 1913.

Joseph Fountain died in 1904 leaving his only surviving son to take over the affairs of the business in which he took little interest. However, Joseph Hewitt seized the opportunity by stepping into the breach as managing director. Hewitt previously represented certain banking interests at the time of the merger of the new company while practising as a Barnsley solicitor in which role he had become well versed in colliery matters having risen from nothing to solicitor and on to be managing director and director of a number of colliery companies.

Born in 1867 in Barnsley, he attended St. Mary's Church of England School for Boys and gained a scholarship to Barnsley Grammar School. In due course he became a junior clerk to a firm of solicitors, Newman and Bond. Eventually he became articled, qualifying as a solicitor at the age of twenty-six in 1893.

During the 1890s, he became associated with the management of collieries until his subsequent involvement as solicitor and trustee to Fountain and Burnley in 1896. He later became a director of George Fountain and Son, who were owners of Haigh Colliery, and in 1916, when the colliery was taken over by the Fountains, he was chairman of the board of the Wharncliffe Woodmoor Coal Company. He also formed the South Yorkshire Coal Owners Association, which by 1912 represented collieries employing over 11,000 miners.

During the First World War his expertise in coal mining matters was fully utilised by the government. Joseph also had army connections. In 1910 he received a commission, attaining the rank of captain with the Yorkshire and Lancashire Regiment in 1914.

In 1918 he became a magistrate, a knight in 1919 and a baronet in 1921. Lieutenant Colonel Sir Joseph Hewitt, Bart., JP died in 1923 at the age of fifty-six at his home at Ouslethwaite Hall, Barnsley.

Certainly his was a lifetime of achievement, but it was not until after his death that it was discovered that he had been receiving salary increases with regard to the Wharncliffe Woodmoor Colliery from £500 in 1916 rising to £5,000 per annum in 1923 in addition to charging heavy expenses and legal fees from the company amounting to over £25,000. It would appear that there were some questions which could no longer be answered about the sanctioning of these payments. It was in complete contrast to a miner's earnings of five shillings [25p] a day in the Wheatley Wood pit at Woolley Colliery.

The new owners supported the needs of the miners' and their families' educational interests, colliers' holiday trips, financial support to Beckett Hospital in Barnsley, the Leeds Eye Hospital and other associated worthy causes, including an association for promoting kindness to the pit ponies.

Immediately before the war the company found it necessary to sink deeper shafts and open up new areas in order to produce coal after exploratory borings were made at Woolley in 1909.

In January 1910, the site for two new sixteen foot diameter shafts was agreed by Miss Annie Fountain, now the principal shareholder in the company, who cut the first sods. The shafts went down to the Parkgate, Thorncliffe, Silkstone and Blocking seams which were worked from 1912 and through the war. The board also decided to build one hundred new houses for the Woolley colliers.

The Company continued to operate until nationalisation in 1947.

CHAPTER SIX

Railways in and Around Barnsley

One hundred and fifty years ago railways were beginning to show an important potential for the movement of coal. At this time the Manchester, Sheffield and Lincolnshire Railway (MS&LR), successor to the South Yorkshire Railway had the monopoly, which threatened the Midland Railway. The latter were seeking to install a direct line through the coalfields from Sheffield to Barnsley and in 1890 had succeeded in obtaining government sanction for a four and a half mile branch from Wincobank in Sheffield to Chapeltown. Not surprisingly Newton, Chambers and Company, whose coal and iron industries dominated the area, were interested in developments. Considerable opposition was met from the MS&LR and the Great Northern Railway who had the monopoly of supplying London with South Yorkshire coal originating on the MS&LR.

Newton, Chambers owned Thorncliffe Ironworks at Chapeltown and its associated collieries and coking plants and was initially a fierce opponent, but as the first Lord Wharncliffe was vice chairman of Newton, Chambers and also chairman of the MS&LR, he would no doubt have realised the full business potential of a working agreement to commence the construction at Wincobank of the Chapeltown Branch on the Midlands Sheffield and Rotherham line with an extension from Chapeltown to the Thorncliffe Ironworks. In 1893 the construction from Wincobank ran through the valley of the Blackburn Brook and was laid with double tracks to cope with additional passenger traffic.

The granting of a branch to Barnsley would now provide the Midland Railway with an alternative route between Sheffield and Leeds, as opposed to the established Rotherham and Swinton route. The Midland connection to Thorncliffe was proving to be very successful with the carriage of raw materials.

In 1892 Newton, Chambers entered into an agreement with the Midland to construct a line connecting the Chapeltown Branch to their colliery at Smithy Wood with a short spur off the High Level branch to link into the Thorncliffe Ironworks and the drift colliery, and also for connection at Thorncliffe to Silkstone Colliery near Westwood.

Newton, Chambers were always seeking ways of exploiting ways of

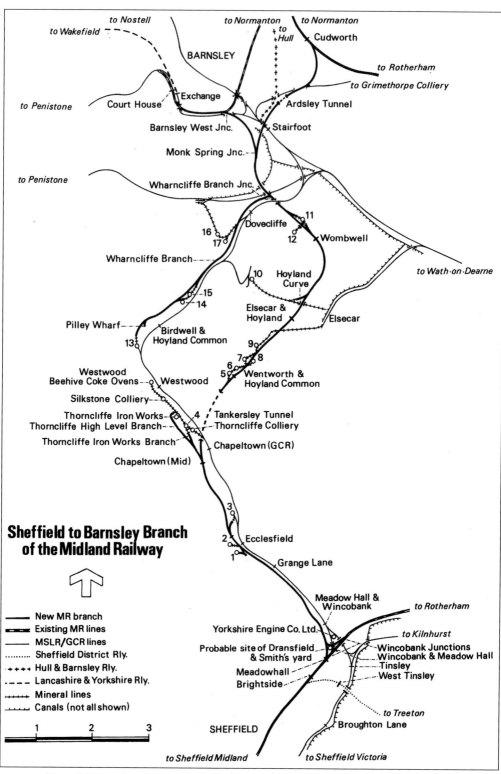

Map of Midland Railway's Sheffield to Barnsley Branch and neighbouring lines.

gaining total control at little cost to themselves. After all, they owned the land on which a variety of other industries stood, with their ironworks manufacturing rails and bridge supports. Yet they were constantly seeking ways of imposing levies on the rail companies, despite bringing good business to Thorncliffe.

The four mile section of construction between Chapeltown and Wombwell was not without problems: the lengthy 1,498 yards long Tankersley tunnel north of Chapeltown and a 200 yard long viaduct between Elsecar, the village of Jump and another north of Wombwell over the Worsborough Dale was no exception.

Contractors Scott and Middleton carried out the task of constructing the tunnel and viaducts and the work was completed in 1896. The company owned a fleet of small steam locomotives which were used on the Chapletown branch extension. The locomotive used at Thorncliffe Drift Pit was aptly renamed 'Tankersley' and continued in service until 1955 when the pit closed.

The three and a quarter mile long single goods line on the Wharncliffe branch to Birdwell and Pilley just north of Wombwell opened in September 1897, passing close to several large collieries, but it was not until the June of 1898 that Newton, Chambers came to an agreement with the Midland Railway to connect their Rockingham Colliery at Birdwell with the Wharncliffe Branch.

Nine collieries, three of which belonged to Thorncliffe, were subsequently linked with the railway which included the Wharncliffe Branch.

During the 1920s considerable changes took place with the introduction of large batteries of coke ovens from which by-products were obtained thus resulting in the concentration of coke production at Wharncliffe Silkstone, Barrow and Smithy Wood, Barnsley Main and Wombwell collieries. The Smithy Wood coking plant was not connected to the former Midland Branch but received its coal from Thorncliffe and Rockingham Collieries by aerial flight, thus dispatching its product via the former MS&LR Sheffield to Barnsley line.

However, in 1929 the London Midland and Scottish Railway (LMS), renamed in the 1923 re-grouping of the railway companies, lost considerable coke traffic as a result of the closure of Newton, Chambers coke ovens at Thorncliffe and Rockingham, which also had its effect on the Hoyland Silkstone Colliery.

In 1925 underground workings were merged between Hoyland Silkstone and Rockingham collieries with the Hoyland Silkstone shafts being retained for ventilation, winding of men and materials.

Elsecar and Hoyland Common Station.

Rockingham was used for coal raising.

By 1942 Thorncliffe's last blast furnace was shut down to reduce the glare during air raids, which, as a result, caused deterioration of the lining of the furnace. Thus was ended 150 years of iron smelting.

The majority of deep mines originally connected with the branch were still producing coal on Vesting Day (1 January 1947), although most were closed by the National Coal Board during the 1950s and 1960s when the coal reserves were exhausted.

The Wharncliffe branch between Pilley and Birdwell closed in 1954 and the Wharncliffe branch sidings in 1958, which resulted in traffic from Barrow and Rockingham being re-routed over former MS&LR metals into Wath marshalling yard for onward transit.

Similar elimination of duplicate railhead facilities at Wombwell Main took coal traffic off the former Midland line and into Wath.

Diesel replaced steam and by 1970 the standard British Rail 16-

ton mineral wagons were replaced by merry-go-round hoppers conveying coal to power stations while the only remaining colliery at Skiers Spring was still served by the ex-Midland line until it too closed in 1975. With the loss of coal and coke freight traffic, other chemical and bulk oil products served as a replacement but unfortunately became short lived as a result of the closure of the Shell Mex and British Petroleum refinery in Cheshire around 1980.

Passenger traffic throughout had always been a secondary consideration, but the Barnsley branch to Sheffield and Cudworth continued to operate until 1953 when local trains on the former MS&LR line, Sheffield (Victoria) to Barnsley (Exchange), were withdrawn.

During the 1950s through trains were routed via the link from Monk Spring junction to Cudworth, avoiding Barnsley, to join up with the Midland main line but this ceased in 1964, largely due to the deterioration of Ardsley tunnel. It was, however, reopened for freight trains when a newly constructed spur connected in 1967 via the former Hull and Barnsley line to Stairfoot. This only lasted until 1979.

Although the ex-Midland passenger stations remained open, Wentworth closed in 1959 and Ecclesfield in 1967.

In 1983 the Barnsley – Penistone line reopened, while the Sheffield to Barnsley line continues to thrive with frequent links to Leeds, Wakefield and Huddersfield.

Little remains of the Wharncliffe branch today with whole areas being landscaped or, as in so many cases today, being replaced by industrial estates. This marked the end of coal freight traffic. Only the transportation of passengers remains. Thus we come to the end of an era.

CHAPTER SEVEN

Trade Unions

Miners have fought for better wages and working conditions for the past 200 years.

Early records mention a Coal Miners' Society in West Yorkshire when, in 1792, colliers employed by the Duke of Norfolk refused to work at the Sheffield pits until their wages were raised.

In 1842 the Mining Association of Great Britain and Ireland (MAGB&I) was formed. It was the same year in which the *Coal Mines Act* came into force making it illegal for mine owners to employ women or boys under the age of ten to work underground. Two years later the Association led a five month strike for better wages, but pressure from coal owners and the government brought the matter to an end.

1858 saw the amalgamation of the South and West Miners' Association, now renamed as the Yorkshire Miners' Association, which gave more strength to the mining work force, and put further pressure on owners and the government to improve conditions.

One aspect of the government and owners' safety intervention came about in 1862 with the introduction of upcast shafts for ventilation and a secondary means of escape at all collieries after the Hartley colliery disaster in Northumberland in which 204 miners lost their lives.

In spite of this, safety precautions, mining disasters and conditions remained absolutely appalling and the following year the Miners' National Union succeeded the MAGB&I.

This new union was short lived and was replaced by the Miners' Federation of Great Britain in November 1889. John Normansell, a town councillor, was elected secretary of the Yorkshire miners and Ben Ricard of the Yorkshire Miners' Association as the first President of the MFGB.

In 1893 mine owners demanded a 25 per cent cut in miners' pay which resulted in a lock-out which lasted for six weeks.

At Featherstone in the West Riding of Yorkshire, soldiers from a local barracks marched on the colliery and opened fire on the crowd killing two men and wounding sixteen. This tragic event, known as the 'Featherstone Riot', gained public sympathy and the owners were forced to restore wage cuts fifteen weeks later.

Miners demonstration in Barnsley, 17 June 1907.

At the turn of the century, the minimum limit for underground work was raised to thirteen years of age.

In February 1912 a six-weeks long, nation-wide strike for a minimum wage was called off when the Liberal Government promised to introduce protective legislation on pay, but after the miners returned to work the government reneged on its promise.

In 1914, at the outbreak of the First World War, the coal owners demanded a repeal of the eight-hours legislation, curtailment of holidays and higher productivity for the war effort.

After the Armistice of 1918, the government still remained in control but it was not long before the MFGB were making demands for a six-hour day and a 30 per cent wage increase for the miners. A breakdown in negotiations led to a ballot vote in favour of strike action.

Coal picking in Barnsley during the 1912 strike by miners.

The Sankey Commission, comprising of the government, MFGB and mine owners' representatives came to an agreement for a wage increase and reduction in the number of working hours. The strike was called off, but again the agreement was not honoured by the government, who, having been in control for the previous six years, decided to return control of the pits to their owners in 1921.

The year brought about a 'slump' resulting in coal owners threatening a 50 per cent cut in miners' pay. The MFGB opposed and a lock-out followed on 1 April. Once again the government re-imposed the Emergency Powers Act and drafted the army into the coalfields.

After three months an agreement was reached for a reduction in wages, thus ending the lock-out.

In 1923 the miners fought to abolish this agreement and in June 1925 the coal owners announced that the current wage agreements would end which resulted in a government enquiry being set up on 31 July which made the recommendation of a subsidy to maintain miners' wages at current levels.

The Commission of Inquiry, under Sir Herbert Samuel, did not include miners' representatives. The report was completed and published in March 1926 and favoured the coal owners. This resulted in the issue of an ultimatum to miners to accept reduced wages and thus ended the guaranteed wage agreement and an increase in hours of work.

Owners posted notices on 30 April imposing a lock-out on 1,000,000 miners. The king signed a proclamation declaring Britain to be in a state of emergency.

On 1 May the trade union voted overwhelmingly in favour of a general strike which lasted from 3-12 May and was subsequently called off following a promise from Sir Herbert Samuel that negotiations on miners' pay would resume if the miners returned to work.

The MFGB were opposed to the Trade Union Congress General Council's agreement to this condition and continued the strike relying on food handouts and financial contributions. On 30 November 1926, Yorkshire miners finally returned to work exhausted and feeling betrayed. Thus ended the lock-out which had lasted for seven months.

Unemployment, poor pay and conditions continued into the 1930s when membership of the MFGB fell to half that of the previous ten years.

Again pressure was put on the government to partially reverse the 1926 Samuel Commission findings.

By 1931 unemployment in mining districts had increased up to 41 per cent while employed miners were earning six shillings and ten pence [35p] per day.

Hunger marches followed during the 1930s and in November 1935, a majority vote for strike action by the miners of the MFGB forced the government to reconsider concessions on miners' pay.

With the outbreak of the Second World War the coal industry was once again subject to the Emergency Powers Act and the Essential Works Order of May 1941. However, the old problem of a guaranteed minimum wage cropped up again in 1944 when Yorkshire miners took strike action which forced the government

Barnsley soup kitchen during the miners' strike of 1921.

and coal owners to come to an agreement on this issue. In this same year plans were already taking shape for a nationalised industry of the future, when ownership would be transferred from the private coal owners to a new nationalised body, and at the same time the National Union of Miners was formed.

The war ended in 1945 and on 1 January 1947, known as 'Vesting Day', the coal industry became fully nationalised under the control of the National Coal Board.

The NUM set up a Miners' Charter for modernisation, safety laws, compensation pay for industrial injuries, a five-day working week, adequate pensions at fifty-five years of age, good housing and decent wages.

The situation however, was not to change as private ownership had been replaced by state ownership. The control and management had been left in the hands of managers who had previously been managers or even actual owners.

Coal shortages forced the government and Coal Board to seek an agreement with the NUM to increase production by introducing a sixth working shift on Saturdays. A major strike at Grimethorpe colliery brought about by miners' growing unease over this decision as being a further means to delude miners into another false sense of security.

The period between 1947 and 1957 saw a gradual reduction in the number of working collieries when government policy was that Britain's needs should be met using cheap oil instead of expensive coal and to invest money into a nuclear power programme. The next six years saw the closure of a further 264 collieries throughout the United Kingdom, cutting the work force by 30 per cent.

The decline of the coal mining industry continued with the closure of a further 300 collieries so that by 1968 only 320,000 miners still remained.

Many coalfield leaders such as Yorkshireman Jock Kane always advocated the introduction of a common wage agreement throughout the entire coal industry.

An unofficial strike in Yorkshire over a demand for an eight-hour day for surface workers led to 130,000 miners nation-wide coming out in support. Chairman of the NCB, Lord Robens, agreed to the introduction of the eight-hour day for surface workers on condition that the strikers returned to work.

The problems involving pit closures, job losses and low wages continued into the early 1970s with failed negotiations between the NUM and the NCB resulting in overtime bans and strike action on 9 January 1972. A state of emergency was once again declared by the government and a public enquiry was set up by Lord Wilberforce with a recommendation for wage increases thus ending the strike after seven weeks.

The following year further overtime bans were introduced in support of wage claims and again a state of emergency was declared aimed at limiting the industry to a three-day working week.

A further strike followed in February 1974 when once again the miners' case for improved pay and conditions was put before the government.

A general election brought about a change of government with Labour in power which resulted in a Pay Board's recommendation for substantial wage increases and other benefits. The strike ended on 11 March.

A new plan 'Plan for Coal' emerged which included expansion and development of the coal mining industry with the opening up of the

Selby Coalfield in Yorkshire.

1979 saw another change in government with the Conservatives back in power. The new plan for expansion and development was put into reverse with the government authorising a pit closure programme in 1981.

Yet again, in 1983, an overtime ban was called in protest to the threat of further pit closures and job losses. Cortonwood colliery was earmarked for closure, together with others, which sparked off the 1984-85 miners' strike.

The dispute, which lasted sixteen months, was probably the worst in the history of the coal mining industry. 11,000 miners were arrested, 7,000 injured, eleven died and over 1,000 were sacked and colliery entrances became battlefields between pickets and police.

At Orgreave colliery in June and July 1984, 10,000 miners faced 8,000 police armed with riot gear.

The odds against the NUM were overwhelming with coal being imported into Britain and union funds exhausted.

The strike finally ended, but even then four months of partial strike action in the form of an overtime ban continued.

The strike was not for wages but for the principle that miners' jobs should be preserved for future generations and not destroyed by continuous pit closures.

Since the 1984-85 strike seventy-nine pits throughout the United Kingdom were closed with a loss of over 100,000 jobs.

There are no winners and losers for the coal industry which was bound to fall into a decline with the importation of cheaper coal and the advancement of technology to replace coal with other sources of energy.

In December 1995 British Coal became denationalised and the remaining pits once again returned to private ownership, after forty-eight years with Yorkshire still operating a large share of the remaining coal mining industry.

CHAPTER EIGHT

The Collieries of Barnsley

BARLEY HALL COLLIERY

There is little documentation on this colliery which was located at Thorpe Hesley near Rotherham.

A shaft was sunk to a depth of 165 yards in 1886-87 with a surface drift for coal for preparation at Smithy Wood Colliery after transportation by road.

During the 1970s, 379 men were producing an output of 173,000 tons per year from the Low Fenton seam.

The colliery closed in 1974.

Accidents: None are recorded.

BARNSLEY MAIN COLLIERY

Owners: Barnsley Main Colliery Co. Ltd, later to become Barrow Barnsley Collieries Ltd.

Location: Barnsley.

History: The first shaft was sunk in 1838, developing into the No. 2 downcast fifteen feet diameter shaft to a depth of 512 yards. A fourth upcast sixteen feet diameter shaft was sunk to a depth of 640 yards, and a third shaft at Old Oaks was the pumping station.

Early seams worked were Ardsley and Haigh Moor and later Parkgate, Fenton and Thorncliffe, producing an annual output of 600,000 tons of steam, house and gas coal in 1927.

Further development in No. 2 downcast shaft in December 1945 proceeded so rapidly that on 1 December 1946, just before nationalisation, output reached 1,000 tons a day in one shift.

The colliery closed in 1991.

Accidents: 16-17 February 1942, thirteen miners were killed in an explosion caused by the ignition of firedamp by flash from a coal cutting trailing cable.

Again, on 7 May 1947, nine miners lost their lives in another explosion caused by ignition of firedamp by an arc forming between the core of a trailing cable and the moving rocker arm of the conveyor.

Today the colliery headgear and winding house stands as a memorial.

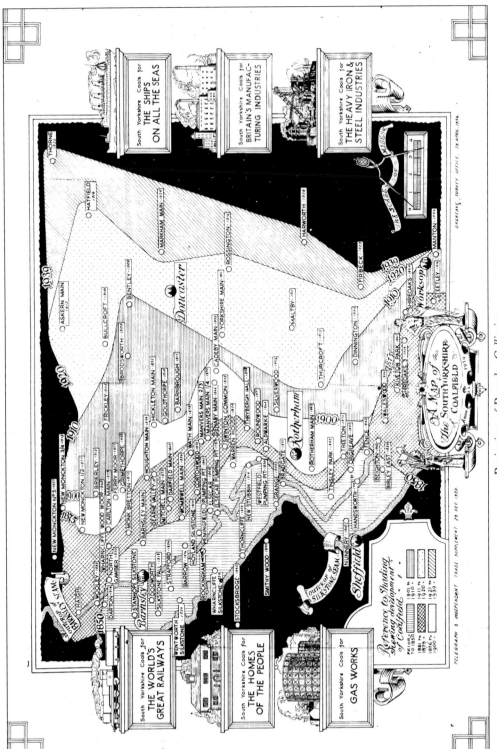

Beginnings of Barnsley Collieries.

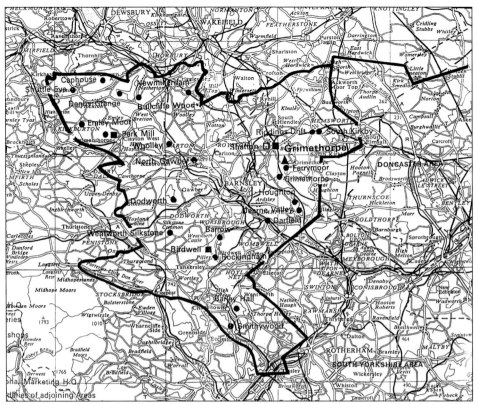

National Coal Board Map of Barnsley Area Collieries (1971).

BARROW COLLIERY

Owners: Barrow Hematite Steel Co. Ltd, Barnsley, later to become Barrow Barnsley Main Collieries Ltd.

Location: Worsborough Bridge near Barnsley.

History: Two shafts were sunk to a depth of 372 yards in 1875, with a common pit bottom for coal output at 335 yards. A third shaft sunk at the same time to a depth of 308 yards was used for winding men and materials.

The colliery was known as Barrow No. 1, employing 1,384 men underground and Barrow No. 2, with 868 underground. 576 men on the surface covered the work of both pits in 1910. This increased to 2,060 underground and 400 on the surface during the late 1920s, but reduced the underground work force by half by the mid 1940s.

Modernisation took place during the 1970s which allowed 1,313 employees to produce 693,000 tons annually assisted by 100 per cent mechanised workings in Lidgett,

Barrow Colliery, scene of Pit Cage disaster on 15 November 1907.

Thorncliffe, Parkgate and Silkstone seams developed at Swallow Wood. All the seams, except Lidgett and Fenton, had been worked for several decades when annual production was only 600,000 tons of coking, gas, household and steam coal.

The colliery closed after the miners' strike of 1984-5.

Accidents: Barrow Colliery is well known for a disastrous accident which occurred on 15 November 1907, when seven men lost their lives by being hurled from a double-decker cage to the bottom of the pit shaft. Nine others were injured in the accident.

Seven men were killed (pictured) when they were hurled from a double-decker cage to the bottom of the pit shaft at Barrow Colliery, Worsborough near Barnsley, on 15 November 1907. Nine other cage occupants received injuries.

The official report reads:

The accident occurred in the 17 foot upcast shaft which is used for the raising and lowering of men from the Parkgate, Thorncliffe and Silkstone seams which are 372, 410 and 480 yards from the surface respectively.

There are two cages in the shaft, each running on three rope guides with a balance rope attached to the bottoms of the cages to ensure smooth running. On the day of the accident, a cage containing 17 men, 12 on the top deck and five on the bottom, was lowered to the Thorncliffe seam from the Parkgate 38 yards above, so that one of the number in the top deck could get off at the Thorncliffe before the remainder were raised to the surface. This man stepped across the space at the top staging without waiting for the flag (hinged sheets of iron fixed at the edge of each staging) to be dropped. The onsetter, without checking, gave the signal for the cage to be raised whilst the onsetter on the bottom staging at the same time dropped the flag without communicating with the onsetter above.

The result was when the cage was raised it swung free striking several girders before being stopped by the engineman. Seven men were violently thrown out of the cage, falling to their deaths on the pit bottom. The cage crumpled but held, thus saving the lives of the others, although had the cage been fitted with gates the men may well have been saved. Both onsetters were blamed for the accident. Another nine suffered serious injury but survived.

BULLCLIFFE WOOD COLLIERY

Owners: Bullcliffe Wood Colliery Co. Ltd.

Location: Bretton West (according to NCB records), near Wakefield. (Usually known as West Bretton)

History: The colliery was established in 1927, when it was known as Bullcliffe Old Lane Colliery, as 1945 records show, employing 109 underground and thirty-one men on the surface.

In 1956 Bullcliffe Wood became established as a drift mine with two of the drifts at a gradient of one-in-four, one being 405 yards and the other 469 yards long. The former was equipped with a thirty-six inch conveyor serving directly into a bunker and the latter being used for ventilation and access.

During the 1970s, 297 employees were producing 230,000 tons annually for the Top Haigh Moor and Low Haigh Moor seams.

The colliery closed in 1985.

Accidents: None are recorded.

CAPHOUSE COLLIERY

Owners: Lockwood and Elliott.

Location: Wakefield.

History: Two coal seams were leased in the Flockton area by James Milnes from the Countess of Bute in 1778.

In 1827 the lease was taken over by Sir John Lister Lister [sic] Kaye of Denby Grange from Lord Wharncliffe. The old shafts were deepened by sixteen yards to the Flockton Thin seam. Sir John had an interest in a number of collieries, known as Denby Grange Collieries, which included Victoria, Prince of Wales, Alexandra and Blossom pits extending to Hope and Inman pits in the 1850s.

By 1850 the Flockton Thin seam was exhausted and the shaft was further deepened to the Old Hards seam which in turn became exhausted in 1865.

In 1854 Caphouse and Hope pits were linked to the Lancashire and Yorkshire Railway by a specially constructed mineral line known as the Sir John line.

In 1876 Caphouse shaft was deepened to the New Hards seam for the last time, and a steam winding engine, probably acquired from a Lancashire textile mill, was installed. The owner was Emma Lister Kaye. A stone plaque above the doorway of the winding engine house bore her initials.

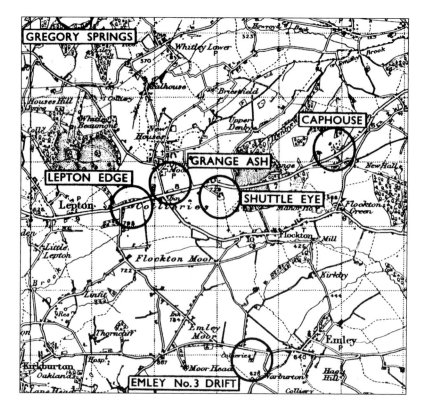

Caphouse Colliery, National Mining Museum for England. 1994.

At the same time a furnace upcast shaft was sunk which became defunct when a connection was made through to Hope Pit which had a ventilating fan.

At some stage between 1885 and 1913 the Hope Pit New Hards seam became exhausted and was subsequently deepened to reach the Wheatley Lime seam.

In 1917 the colliery was purchased by a company in which a local

Caphouse Colliery, National Mining Museum for England. 1999.

mining engineer, Percy Greaves, had an interest. His father had been the manager of Caphouse.

By 1942 the colliery had been resold to Lockwood and Elliott, when the development of the Beeston seam, via an inclined drift and Hope shaft, was commenced.

After nationalisation traditional methods of hand filling and pick and shovel mining continued until 1977, although partial mechanisation was introduced in 1962 with a chain-hauled plough and shearers when the Wheatley Lime seam was abandoned.

There was a great increase in output when the surface drift to the Beeston seam was completed. In 1978 this was exploited at the neighbouring Denby Grange Colliery.

The following year two drifts were driven up through the faults of Beeston seam at Denby Grange. In October 1981 the two collieries amalgamated, resulting in an average annual increase in output from 100,000 to 250,000 tons with a further increase of 500,000 tons from working the Denby Grange area.

Denby Grange Colliery was connected to Bullcliffe Wood Colliery by two drifts and amalgamated in 1985. In turn Bullcliffe was connected through to Woolley Colliery. The first coal from Denby Grange was conveyed to Woolley in March 1985 and in October of that year the last coal was conveyed out of Caphouse surface drift.

Caphouse became the home of the Yorkshire Mining Museum in 1986 and opened to the public on 6 June 1988.

In June 1995 the museum gained national status by becoming the National Coal Mining Museum for England.

Accidents: None are recorded.

DARFIELD MAIN COLLIERY

Owners: Mitchell Main Colliery Co. Ltd.

Location: Wombwell near Barnsley.

History: Two shafts were sunk in 1860 to a depth of 342 yards. A third shaft 627 yards deep, was added later, which was used for winding all coal from the Beamshaw level at 224 yards.

During the 1970s, 875 men produced an annual output of 241,000 tons when the pit was fully mechanised.

The colliery closed in 1989.

Accidents: None are recorded.

DEARNE VALLEY COLLIERY

Owners: Dearne Valley Colliery Co. Ltd.

Location: Approximately five miles east of Barnsley, in the shadow of Houghton Main.

History: A surface drift was established in 1903 on the outcrop with subsequent development of roadways. Coal was taken to Houghton to be weighed and drawn out of the pit by an endless haulage system.

The longwall method of cutting, firing and filling of coal faces was never put into operation and so there were no rippers or machine men working at the colliery until power loading was introduced in 1965.

During the 1970s, 406 men produced an annual output of 185,000 tons using fully mechanised equipment in the Shafton seam.

The colliery closed in 1991.

Accidents: None are recorded.

DENBY GRANGE COLLIERY previously known as PRINCE OF WALES

Owners: Denby Grange Collieries Ltd.

Location: Netherton near Wakefield.

History: The colliery was established in 1894 when two shafts of 171 and 164 yards deep were sunk. The ventilation was provided by a 1,200 yard long drift. The mine was also linked to Caphouse Colliery.

During the 1970s output reached 87,000 tons annually by a total of 267 men.

The colliery closed in 1991.

Accidents: None are recorded.

DODWORTH COLLIERY

Owners: Old Silkstone Collieries Ltd, Dodworth, Barnsley.

Location: Dodworth.

History: The Colliery was originally known as Church Lane pit, later to become Old Silkstone Colliery and finally Dodworth Colliery when it was nationalised in 1947.

Shafts Nos. 2 and 3 were sunk in 1850 to work the Silkstone seam. Each was twelve feet in diameter. No. 2, the downcast, was 258 yards deep and No. 3, the upcast, 262 yards deep. Both were used for man-riding and materials.

Nearby Redbrook shaft, with a diameter of ten feet was sunk in 1903 to a depth of 518 yards. It was also downcast and used for man-riding and materials. The Higham pumping shaft, twelve feet in diameter and 203 yards deep, was also a downcast.

The man-riding installation in the Redbrook section served the

1,250 yards Fenton seam and the installation at Dodworth served the 1,600 yards Whinmoor seam.

Other seams worked were Top Haighmoor, Fenton, Whinmoor and Silkstone. Top Haighmoor had two faces extracting thirty-eight inches of coal, Fenton one face extracting fifty inches of coal, Whinmoor had three faces extracting thirty-six inches of coal whilst Silkstone was undergoing development.

Under nationalisation Higham became a satellite unit whose output surfaced through a drift and was conveyed overland to Dodworth on cable belt conveyors at which time 1,396 men were producing 721,000 tons annually from the Whinmoor and Silkstone seams.

1910 EMPLOYMENT FIGURES AT PITS OWNED BY OLD SILKSTONE COLLIERIES LTD SURROUNDING DODWORTH

	Underground	Surface	Seams Worked
1910			
Dodworth, Parkgate	644		Flockton, Parkgate
Dodworth, Thorncliffe	594	251	Thorncliffe pumping
Higham	-	8	Station
Redbrook	-	-	Standing
Silkstone Fall	137	19	Parkgate
1927			
Dodworth	880	148	
Silkstone	200	40	
1945			
Dodworth	1085	296	Silkstone Four Foot Flockton, Parkgate &Thorncliffe pumping station
Higham			Pumping station
Silkstone Fall			Silkstone Four Foot

The colliery closed in 1987.

Accidents: On 15 February 1860, thirteen miners were killed in an explosion at Higham due to ignition of firedamp caused by a naked candle.

EMLEY MOOR

Owners: Stringer and Jagger Ltd, later to become Stringer and Son Ltd.

Location: Emley, near Huddersfield.

History: Established about 1850.

In 1910 Emley No. 3 Drift near to Wakefield was employing 660 men underground and 173 on the surface.

During nationalisation the shaft was increased to a depth of 128 yards for the use of men and materials and two surface drifts, including the mine at Skelmanthorpe which was equipped with a thirty inch conveyor, delivering coal to a preparation plant two miles distant from the colliery.

At this time Emley Moor was producing an annual output of 100,000 tons of coal from the Blocking and Beeston seams employing 287 men.

The Colliery closed in 1985.

Accidents: None are recorded.

FERRYMOOR COLLIERY

Owners: Hodroyd Coal Co. Ltd. Barnsley.

Location: Grimethorpe.

History: Shafts were sunk in 1915 and 1916 to a depth of seventy-two yards. The pillar and stall system was operated until 1965 but the pit became entirely mechanised in later years, when output was conveyed to the surface via Riddings Drift mine.

At that time an annual output of 144,000 tons was worked from the Shafton seam using a workforce of 347 men.

The colliery closed in 1988.

Accidents: None are recorded.

GRIMETHORPE COLLIERY

Owners: Carlton Main Colliery Co. Ltd, Barnsley.

Location: Grimethorpe near Barnsley.

The development of Grimethorpe as a Colliery was started in 1894 by the Mitchell Main Coal Company when No. 1 and No. 2 shafts were sunk, and the first coal was worked in the Barnsley seam in 1897. During nationalisation the deepest shaft was extended to 926 yards.

Major combined mine reconstruction was completed

New style headgear at Grimethorpe, c.1970.

New style headgear at Grimethorpe, c.1970.

in 1963 which enabled nearby Houghton colliery output to be wound and prepared, with one shaft dealing with output from the upper coal seams of both collieries, while the other worked the lower seams. All the working faces were fully mechanised with a workforce of 2,088 men producing an annual output of 488,000 tons from the Parkgate, Low Beamshaw and Meltonfield seams.

The colliery closed in 1992 just prior to the making of the film, *Brassed Off,* which featured the story of miners of Grimley Colliery (Grimethorpe) and their colliery band at the time when collieries were facing the threat of uncertainty and closure.

Accidents: None are recorded.

An extract from the *Barnsley Chronicle* dated Saturday, 13 October, 1894, gives an account of that memorable day of Turning The First Sod at Grimethorpe.

> *Familiar as one is in this district with coal pits and with mining operations on an extensive scale, the starting of a new colliery, is an event of sufficient importance to arouse a feeling of lively and wide spread interest. Not only is it an affair of great moment to the promoters of the enterprise, and to those engaged in similar*

Cutting the first sod at Grimethorpe, 8 October 1894.

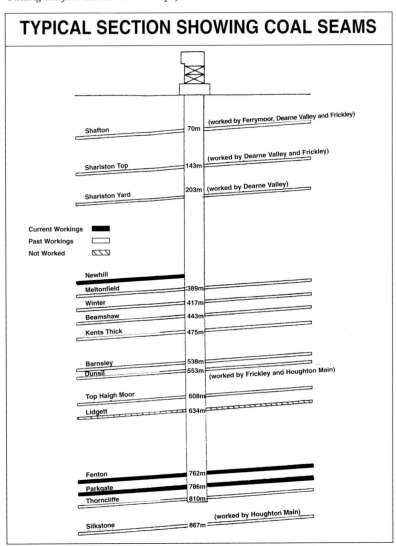

TYPICAL SECTION SHOWING COAL SEAMS

Seam	Depth	Note
Shafton	70m	(worked by Ferrymoor, Dearne Valley and Frickley)
Sharlston Top	143m	(worked by Dearne Valley and Frickley)
Sharlston Yard	203m	(worked by Dearne Valley)

Current Workings ■
Past Workings ▭
Not Worked ▨

Seam	Depth	Note
Newhill		
Meltonfield	:389m	
Winter	417m	
Beamshaw	443m	
Kents Thick	475m	
Barnsley	538m	
Dunsil	553m	(worked by Frickley and Houghton Main)
Top Haigh Moor	608m	
Lidgett	634m	
Fenton	762m	
Parkgate	786m	
Thorncliffe	810m	
		(worked by Houghton Main)
Silkstone	867m	

undertakings, but it means employment for a large number of people who derive their livelihood from coal-getting, while other branches of industry in the locality of the new colliery also receive, as a rule, a tremendous fillip.

Instances are common enough hereabouts of sleepy, out of the way villages being suddenly transformed into busy centres of population through the sinking of a coal pit. Such a change, there is every reason to believe, will shortly be experienced by the village of Grimethorpe, in the township of Brierley, where, on Monday last, the ceremony of cutting the first sod in connection with a new mining venture, to be known as the Grimethorpe Colliery, took place, in the presence of a numerous company.

The new sinking is the enterprise of the Mitchell Main Colliery Co. Limited, which has already two important collieries at work in the neighbourhood. The site of the Grimethorpe Colliery is on the estate of Mr. F.J.S. Foljambe, of Osherton Hall, being close to Grimethorpe village and Ferry Moor; while Cudworth, Great Houghton, Shafton-two-Gates and Darfield are also near to hand. It is expected that the Barnsley seam will be reached at a depth of about 500 yards and the total area of the new coal field is over 3000 acres.

The two shafts which are about to be sunk will be of a clear diameter of 19 feet inside. The water bearing strata, of which there may be a considerable extent to pass through, will be tubbed back in the usual way with cast iron, and after this part of the work has been got through the sinking and bricking will be continued simultaneously. It is anticipated that the Barnsley bed will be reached in about two years' time.

The colliery will be fitted with the best modern appliances, and be capable when completed of drawing 2,500 tons a day. This, with the output at the other two collieries, Mitchell Main and Darfield Main, will make a total yield of at least a million tons per annum, so that the Mitchell Main Colliery Co. will be one of the largest coal producing corporations in South Yorkshire. The Grimethorpe sinking is about three miles distant, in a north-easterly direction, from the Mitchell Main Colliery, but the royalties are connected.

For the transport of the mineral, adequate railway facilities will be available. The Midland Co. have already laid down a branch between the new colliery and their main line, the junction being affected about a mile beyond Cudworth station; and the M.S.&L. are making arrangements to connect with their Houghton and Stairfoot branch.

There was a large and representative company to witness the sod-turning on Monday, invitations having been issued to over 100 persons. Those accepting assembled at Cudworth Railway Station early in the afternoon, and were conveyed by special train, made up of saloon and first-class carriages, along the new line, to see the scene of operations. The afternoon was fine, the party in good spirits, and there was not a little joking about this 'first trip to Grimethorpe'. A crowd of people from the adjacent villages awaited the arrival of the train. The party having alighted a move was at once made to the spot where the shafts are to be sunk, indicated by a hoisted flag, and by two large circles marked out on the turf with a white post in the centre of each.

A ring was formed round what will be the down-cast shaft, those present including Mr. Joseph Mitchell, Bolton Hall (managing director).

Among a few others present were well known names in the Mining and Railway business at that time. These included:-
Mr. C.F. Rhodes, Aldwarke and Car House Collieries.
Mr. Jos. Longbotham, Barrow Collieries.
Mr. J.W. Brookes, M.S. & L. Railway Company.
Mr. John Mitchell, Swaithe Hall.
In the absence of Mr. Foljambe, the first sod was cut by Mr. G.H. Turner, general manager of the Midland Railway Company.

HOUGHTON MAIN COLLIERY

Owners: Houghton Main Colliery Company.
Location: Little Houghton, near Barnsley.
History: Two shafts were sunk between 1873 and 1878 at Little Houghton near Barnsley, shaft No. 1, the downcast to the Barnsley seam and No. 2, the upcast. A third shaft was sunk in 1924 and deepened to 823 yards between 1937 and 1940 to access the Thorncliffe seam. This eventually became the upcast shaft in 1953, at the same time as a new semi-automated skip winding system was introduced.

In the latter years all the output from the fully mechanised workings was transported underground and wound coal was produced from the Top and Low Beamshaw and Parkgate seams.

During the 1970s 1,540 men were producing 590,000 tons per year.

The colliery closed in 1992.

Police at Houghton Main colliery during the miners' strike of 1893.

Accidents: On 12 December 1930, seven miners were killed in an explosion caused by the ignition of firedamp during shot-firing.

A second explosion occurred on 12 June 1975, which killed five miners when frictional sparking from a defective fan ignited firedamp.

MONK BRETTON COLLIERY

Owners: Monk Bretton Colliery Co. Ltd. Barnsley, later to become Barrow Barnsley Main Collieries Ltd.

Location: Monk Bretton near Barnsley.

History: Two shafts sunk between 1870-1873.

In 1910 the colliery employed 1,282 men underground and 201 on the surface working the Barnsley seam. By the middle of the 1920s the number had been reduced to 695 and 164 respectively, despite working the additional Kents Thick seam yielding coking, gas, household and steam coal.

During the last year of the Second World War the force rose slightly to 811 and 227 with the addition of the working of the Winter and Beamshaw seams.

The National Coal Board continued to work the mine until its closure in 1968.

Accidents: None are recorded.

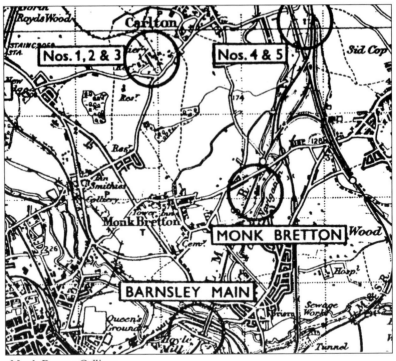

Monk Bretton Colliery.

NEWMILLERDAM COLLIERY
Owners: Newmillerdam Colliery Co. Ltd.
Location: Newmillerdam.
History: This relatively new colliery was established in 1929.

This was a drift mine with output being conveyed direct into the surface screens. Man-riding and return ventilation was provided by a satellite drift.

In 1945 the Winter and Beamshaw seams were worked employing 135 miners underground and only thirty-five on the surface.

During the 1970s 203 men produced 105,000 tons per year from the Kents Thick seam.

The colliery closed in 1981.

Accidents: None are recorded.

NORTH GAWBER COLLIERY
History: North Gawber had a number of early landlords from the seventeenth century until the middle of the nineteenth, when development was encouraged following the arrival of the Lancashire and Yorkshire Railway branch line from Horbury to Barnsley in 1850.

In 1853 a forty-year lease was negotiated by Richard Thorp and his younger brother, the Reverend William Thorp, together with the Wentworth solicitor John Marsden, to enable mining the Barnsley coal bed at Mapplewell on the Wentworth estate. This was finalised in November 1855 when shafts were sunk to the Barnsley seam at a depth of 108 yards, although some records put the date of sinking between 1850 and 1852.

Richard Thorp lived at Banks Hall, Monk Bretton and later at Cockerham Road, Barnsley, where he died in July 1866 at the age of seventy-four. Richard had excellent labour relations with his employees. There are no records of any disputes. His brother William was born at Banks Hall in 1804 and educated at Darton Grammar School before attending Jesus College, Cambridge.

The early workings at North Gawber were in the Barnsley and Mapplewell coal beds but, after a short lived coal boom period, capital was raised and in 1872 a new company, Thorp's Gawber Hall Collieries Ltd, was registered. However, further financial difficulties arose and it was decided to wind up the company in 1881. A year later it was announced that North Gawber was to re-open, with new

North Gawber Colliery.

owners operating under the name of Fountain and Burnley, employing up to 600 miners producing an output of between 1,200 and 1,500 tons a day. Fountain and Burnley retained control until nationalisation in 1947.

In 1910 the colliery employed 662 men underground and 176 on the surface to work the Barnsley seam. By the late 1920s the labour strength decreased, even though working the additional Lidgett, Parkgate, Thorncliffe and Silkstone seams producing an annual 700,000 tons.

The additional Lidgett coal-winding shaft, sunk in 1926, became the centre of the mine which also worked from two surface drifts, thus becoming the focal point of the merger with nearby Darton Colliery in 1948.

The shaft originally sunk to the Barnsley seam, at a depth of 103 yards to excavate the Top and Low Haigh Moor seams, was developed and worked from the Barnsley seam roadways but, at the end of that period, a new connection was driven from the new shaft to these seams. This enabled the total output to be wound from one point. The Lidgett seam went into production in 1930, but since then gradual reconstruction of the colliery plant layout, both underground and on the surface, has taken place.

An extensive belt conveyor system, together with 9,000 yards of mains roadway lighting, was installed underground, while on the surface modern pit-head baths and lamp room were added in 1938.

By the end of the Second World War the Low Haigh and Top Haigh Moor seams were being worked employing 747 miners underground and 179 on the surface.

North Gawber Colliery still continued producing coal after 1947 at the time of nationalisation, thus ending sixty-five years under Fountain and Burnley.

At this time it was decided to wind all coal from the neighbouring Darton Colliery, which worked the same seams and roadways driven into that area, and from both North Gawber and Darton from the upcast shaft of the former. This produced a total daily output of 2,700 tons.

During the period up until its closure in 1986 North Gawber employed 974 miners working the Low Haigh and Top Haigh Moor and Kent Thick seams with an annual output of 344,000 tons.

Accidents: A serious accident took place at North Gawber (Lidgett) on 12 September 1935, when nineteen miners were killed in an explosion of firedamp during shot firing.

PARK MILL COLLIERY

Owners: Stringer and Jagger Ltd, later to become Stringer and Son Ltd.

Location: Clayton West, near Huddersfield.

History: Established between 1850 and 1860.

Two shafts about a mile apart, one being at Park Mill sunk to a depth of seventy-three yards and the other at Springwood were sunk to a depth of eighty-five yards in 1891.

This colliery pioneered coal cutting machines as early as 1880.

By 1927 the colliery had changed its name to Stringer and Sons. In 1945 the Wheatley Lime and New Hards seams were still being worked.

Under nationalisation one of three drifts (with a gradient of one-in-three-and-three-quarters) came into operation in 1952. It was used later during the 1970s for conveying coal from underground locomotion horizon. At this time 309 employees produced 226,000 tons annually from the Low Fenton and Flockton seams, 88 per cent of output being mechanised.

The colliery closed in 1989.

Accidents: None are recorded.

RIDDINGS DRIFT

Located at South Kirkby, this was a new surface drift, opened in April 1970, to the Shafton seam at a depth of 200 yards and ventilated by the South Kirkby upcast shaft and sharing surface facilities. The drift (with a gradient of one-in-four-and-a-third) was 850 yards long and equipment comprised a thirty-six inch cable belt for coal conveying, with a fixed rope hauled car system for the purpose of conveying men and materials.

High rates of productivity were achieved after the drift commenced full production in April 1970.

At that time the planned output of 460,000 tons with 227 men had then reached 409,000 tons.

The colliery closed in 1973.

Accidents: None are recorded.

ROCKINGHAM COLLIERY

Owners: N.C. Thorncliffe Collieries Ltd. (Newton, Chambers).

Location: Situated four miles south of Barnsley, near to the villages of Hoyland Common and Birdwell.

History: In December 1872 Lord Fitzwilliam granted the lease to the Thorncliffe partners, George Newton and Thomas Chambers, to

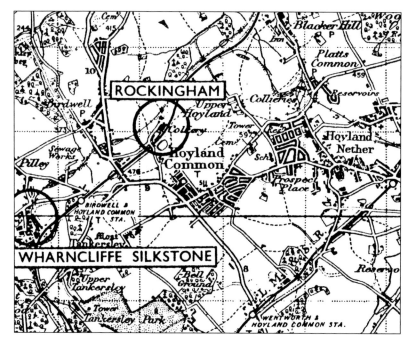

mine 800 acres of coal at £275 per acre for the Silkstone seam and £175 for the Parkgate seam.

Sinking began in June 1873 and continued until 1875 with two of three shafts sunk to a depth of 355 yards for coal winding from the Flockton seam (169 yards) and the Thorncliffe seam (301 yards). The other shaft at Hoyland Silkstone (508 yards) was used as a service shaft from the Top Fenton level.

During sinking operations on 31 March 1875, when reaching the Parkgate seam, shot firing caused the ignition of firedamp and there

Rockingham Colliery, c.1907

was a violent explosion. Both shafts were sealed off but a further explosion resulted in damage to No. 1 headgear and the winding engine house. It took eight weeks before sinking operations were able to continue.

The Thorncliffe partners became a Limited Company known as Newton, Chambers and Company Limited. They named their new colliery Rockingham in honour of the Marquis of Rockingham, a forbear of the Fitzwilliams.

Until 1977 the Rockingham complex consisted of Rockingham, Hoyland Silkstone and Skiers Spring collieries.

Coal mined in the Wharncliffe, Athersley and Rockley areas of the Rockingham colliery was wound up No. 2 shaft and that mined at Hoyland Silkstone was transported on conveyor belts along an underground connecting roadway to Rockingham No. 1 shaft.

Coal mined at Skiers Spring was brought to the surface on conveyor belts up a drift.

Ventilation fans which circulated approximately half a million cubic feet of air per minute were located at Hoyland Silkstone, Skiers Spring and Athersley, ventilating an area of thirty-one miles of underground roadway which included eleven miles of underground conveyor belts.

Water was a constant problem. Approximately 336 million gallons had to be pumped out annually.

During the 1970s 1,453 employees produced 709,000 tons from the Harley, Flockton Thick, Low Fenton and Lidgett seams.

The colliery closed in 1979.

Accidents: None are recorded.

SHUTTLE EYE COLLIERY
Owners: Lockwood and Elliott.

Location: Grange Moor, Wakefield.

History: The colliery was established in about 1862 with two shafts for coal winding at depths of 195 and 288 yards.

In 1962 ventilation, assisted by two drifts at Gregory Spring, was combined with Shuttle Eye. During the 1970s, 222 employees produced 70,000 tons from the Beeston and Black Bed seams.

The colliery closed in 1973.

Accidents: None are recorded.

SMITHY WOOD COLLIERY
Owners: N.C. Thorncliffe Collieries Ltd, later to become Newton, Chambers and Co. Ltd.

Location: Smithy Wood.

History: Established in 1890.

In 1910 the company was known as Newton, Chambers of Thorncliffe, near Sheffield, where the Norfolk and Smithy Wood mines were worked, cutting coal from the Thorncliffe, Thin and Silkstone seams.

By 1927 it was still trading under the name of Newton, Chambers.

During nationalisation the main transport used was a cable belt on an incline of 2,770 yards from the surface. Two shafts and a drift at Thorpe were used for ventilation and the transportation of men and supplies.

All output at that time involved fully mechanised coal faces.

The colliery closed in 1972.

Accidents: None are recorded.

SOUTH KIRKBY COLLIERY

Owners: South Kirkby, Featherstone and Hemsworth Collieries Ltd.

Location: South Kirkby.

History: Originally established in 1880.

During the period of nationalisation two of the three shafts were deepened to a depth of 812 yards and were equipped with balanced skips.

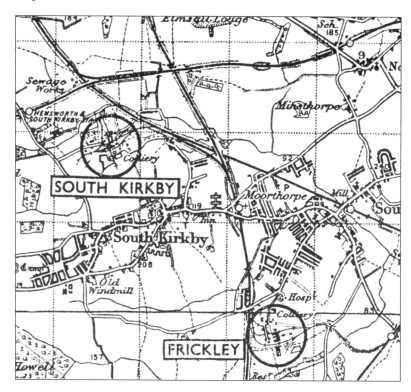

South Kirkby Colliery.

Other shafts at Hemsworth were used for ventilation. During the 1970s the annual output was 736,000 tons from the Meltonfield, Beamshaw and Barnsley seams employing a workforce of 1,992 men.

The colliery closed in 1988.

Accidents: None are recorded.

WENTWORTH SILKSTONE

Owners: Wentworth Silkstone Colliery Ltd.

Location: Stainborough, Barnsley.

History: This colliery originated in 1856. The Wentworth Estate located between Barnsley and Rotherham was one of the two largest landed estates in South Yorkshire during the eighteenth and nineteenth centuries. At its centre stood Wentworth Woodhouse, the residence of the Rockingham and Fitzwilliam families, under which lay the rich reserves of coal of the Barnsley, Parkgate and Silkstone seams.

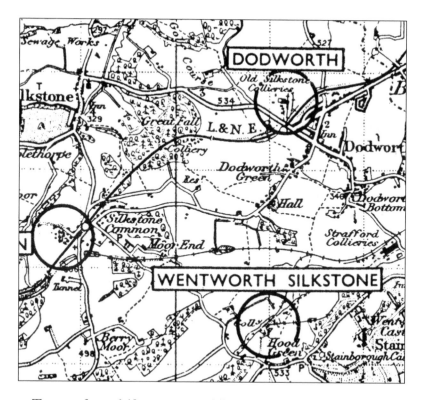

Two surface drifts were established in 1912, and extended between 1955 and 1959, dipping at a gradient of one-in-five to the Whinmoor seam which, in the 1970s, provided all the output, wholly cut and loaded by machines, with an annual production of 384,000 tons. 489 men were employed.

During 1927, 519 men worked underground and eighty-two on the surface. By 1945, 375 were underground and 117 on the surface. Parkgate, Flockton, Fenton and Thorncliffe seams were worked during both those periods.

The colliery closed in 1978.

Accidents: None are recorded.

WOOLLEY COLLIERY

The area known as Woolley Edge, rising from the Dearne Valley, was well known for its abundance of coal. However, it was not until the 1730s that large, new collieries opened up close to the Navigation Canal. Even more followed the increase in industrialisation and population and the opening of the Barnsley

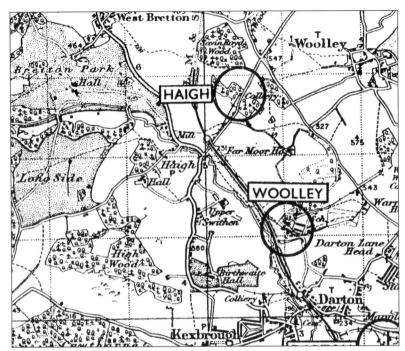

Woolley Colliery, c.1910.

Canal in 1799. The canal went through Darton but because it was one and a half miles from Woolley, a slow decline in the colliery's fortunes followed.

The situation did not improve until a connecting link was made with the South Yorkshire Railway at Barnsley and the Lancashire and Yorkshire Railways so that coal could pass from the Dearne Valley for onward transmission to London and other markets in the 1850s.

In 1852 Godfrey Wentworth of Woolley Hall negotiated for leases on his newly accessible coal. Although he did not directly invest in coal mining, he did indirectly assist the new Woolley Coal Company by making loans, reducing coal rents and building colliers' cottages. In 1853 the Woolley area coals were leased to a partnership under the title of the Woolley Coal Company whose partners and capital holdings were:-

Sir John Lister Lister Kaye of Denby Grange	£12,000
Lister Lister Kaye (Sir John's son) of Denby Grange	£ 3,000
George Lister Lister Kaye (Sir John's brother)	£ 3,000
Godfrey Armytage of Kirklees Hall	£ 3,000
John Marsden, Solicitor	£ 9,000
Total	£30,000

John Marsden was already lawyer and managing partner to the Wentworth Kaye and Armytage families' estates. Educated at Salem Chapel School in George Street, Wakefield, he later became a clerk, at the age of fourteen, in the offices of Foljambe and Dixon of Wakefield, who were attorneys. Thus young John gained an insight into county administration and the coal industry.

Marsden qualified in 1830, which enabled him to set up his own business. He became a magistrates' clerk in 1834, as well as clerk to Geoffrey Wentworth of Woolley Hall and Sir John Lister Lister Kaye, Bart. of Denby Grange, which later proved to be beneficial to his career.

As time progressed Marsden gained access to a wider range of magistrates, most of whom were owners of large estates, and took on estate administration for the Armytages of Kirklees Hall in 1838, all of whom were sitting on wealthy coalfields.

In 1852 he took over as agent for the estates of the Lister Kayes of Denby Grange, who owned a number of working pits, enabling him to move with his family from Croft House near Wakefield to Denby Grange.

John Marsden's role in opening the new colliery at Woolley

included organisation of capital, of which he owned a third, labour, coal production, housing, education, coal marketing and transportation, but it was not without the inherent problems these presented as well as geological matters.

In 1859 Marsden issued the following statement to the miners at Woolley Colliery:

To the workmen at the Woolley Colliery

The Proprietors of the Colliery recommend you, by your sober and steady conduct, to cement the union between themselves and you, and to bear in mind that good Servants make good Masters; and instead of listening to the advice of those who keep you always in an unsettled state, and who live a life of idleness, out of the subscriptions arising from your earnings, and instead of going to the Public-house to spend your earnings, to remain at home and spend your time, out of working hours, in cultivating your Gardens, or in innocent recreation, and to invest any money you can spare in the Savings Bank, to accumulate at Interest; by which means you may hope to save sufficient to keep you in comfort, and independent of the parish, in sickness or old age.

You are also strongly recommended to see that your children have the full benefit of the Day and Sunday School provided for them.

If you do your duty, and are steady and industrious, you may rely on your Masters doing all they constantly can to promote the comfort and happiness of yourselves and your Families.

Woolley Colliery
March 2nd, 1859.

Was this indeed a build up to what was to come? Perhaps.

In January 1861 the colliers at Woolley were given notice to concede a 20 per cent reduction in wages, which resulted in a strike by the men. Marsden informed them that if they struck they would not be re-employed, as indeed they never were. He refused to tolerate any union members.

In March 1861, ninety new hands arrived from Derbyshire to fill vacancies, but they did not stay long. 'Blackleg' labour was employed to replace them. At the same time trouble arose over dirt in the coal.

In April flooding of the workings resulted in only 50,000 tons being produced, half the quantity of the previous year, which resulted in inevitable financial losses.

Later in the same year the Woolley Coal Company joined the newly formed Coalmasters' Association, an early form of trade association, which was started in Barnsley. Members paid subscriptions to cover them during strikes. Until then the colliery had refused to employ union men. Marsden was a committed company man whose main concern was to keep the company going.

By 1862 further capital was needed to pay wages and Marsden surrendered his own life insurance policy to the landlord as security. Further escalation of financial problems followed and the colliery was put up for sale in 1863 for £40,000.

Despite all the financial difficulties of the company, and unable to sell the colliery to a suitable buyer, Marsden somehow managed to keep it going until 1867 when it was finally sold to a limited liability company, the Woolley Coal Co. Ltd, with a capital of £100,000 in £100 shares. Marsden made sure that he was part of this new company, and made a handsome profit in the process as solicitor to previous clients, the Armytages and Saltmarshes, whom he had advised. Marsden became the managing director of this new limited company, receiving a cash sum of £42,874 by way of remuneration.

In 1873 Woolley colliery was sold but little is known about the company who bought it other than it employed more men. In July of that year 360 came out on strike over a proposed 15 per cent reduction in their wages. Labour relations continued to deteriorate despite a flourishing Yorkshire Miners' Association branch at Woolley, but strikes caused the removal of families from colliery villages which caused further hardship.

In 1882 John Marsden was appointed a magistrate before retiring to Hove, on the South Coast, where he died in October 1886.

The first shaft was sunk in 1869 at Wheatley Wood to a depth of 220 yards.

Ownership of the colliery changed to Fountain and Burney in 1894, and in 1912 No. 1 and No. 2 shafts were sunk to a depth of 423 yards. An additional No. 3 shaft was sunk in 1942.

In 1932 the colliery became the first in the country to become fully electrified, and in 1939 pit head baths were opened. Woolley colliery finally closed in 1987.

Accidents: None are recorded.

CHAPTER NINE

The Collieries of Doncaster

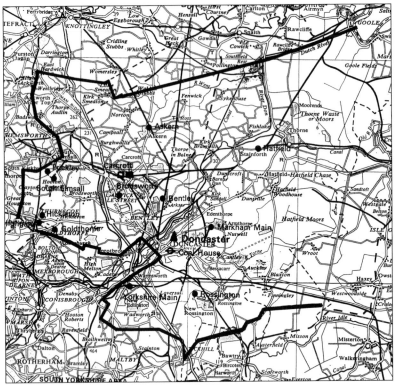

National Coal Board Map of Doncaster Area Collieries (1971).

ASKERN MAIN COLLIERY

Owners: Askern Coal and Iron Co. Ltd, Askern, Doncaster.

Location: Askern.

History: The Askern Coal and Iron Company was formed in March 1910 and established the colliery at Askern, which is situated about seven miles from Doncaster. The first sod was cut on 22 February 1911.

The site chosen for sinking came as a shock to the Askern villagers because the unsightly head frames were too close to the local spa and hydro to enhance their image.

The sinking of two shafts, twenty-one feet six inches in diameter to the Warren House seam was started in April 1911. This was the top section of the Barnsley seam and was reached in September 1912 at a depth of 566 yards in No. 1 shaft and 564 yards in No. 2 shaft. However, there were problems during the sinking of the No. 2 shaft caused by water which was flowing at the rate of fifteen gallons per minute at a depth of only eighteen yards increasing to 3,000 gallons per minute at eighty-six yards, but the strata were free of water below 135 feet.

In 1913 shaft sinking continued to reach the Flockton seam at a depth of 723 yards in No. 1 shaft and 720 yards in No. 2 shaft, and the seam continued to be worked until it was abandoned in 1928. These workings were in the immediate vicinity of the shafts and connected to the Warren House seam by drifts. The second period of working was from 1949 to 1960 when the seam was re-entered before again being abandoned.

The earlier method of working the coal was that of longwall faces divided into

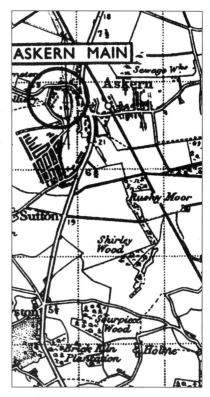

Askern Main Colliery.

Askern Main Colliery, c. 1920.

Askern Main Colliery, c. 1970.

thirty-five yard long tub stalls from which the coal was got by hand, loaded into ten cwt. tubs and hauled by compressed air haulages to the main haulage roads where endless and direct rope haulage systems were used to transport the tubs to the pit bottom.

This method was soon superseded by advancing longwall units with coal cutters undercutting the coal to a depth of six feet. The hand cut coal was then filled out onto shaker pan conveyors into ten cwt. tubs.

Mechanisation took place in the Flockton seam in 1958 with the introduction of an armoured face conveyor and an Anderton Shearer Loader as the coal getting machine.

Underground man-riding and materials haulage to the working faces was by diesel locomotive along a distance of up to four miles of roadway. On the journey outbye some use was made of man-riding conveyor belts to ride men to the vicinity of the diesel locomotive or 'paddy station', as it was commonly known.

Because of the uncertain geology at Askern, use was made of rapid advance headings driven by Dosco Roadheading machines. These headings detect the existence or absence of faulting which could disrupt production units. The units were therefore laid out in such a position to ensure, as far as possible, the minimum of interruption by such faulting.

In 1963 a reconstruction costing £589,000 took place providing underground drivages and extension of trunk conveying to a 350 tons capacity staple shaft bunker, installation of ten tons capacity skips, increasing the belt size on the conveyor system from thirty-six inches to forty-two inches, a 750 tons capacity R.O.M. coal bunker on the surface and a new fan and fan house. The fan was an Aerex type (WF 305/286) with a diameter of 143 inches radial flow powered by a 3,300 volt motor at 455 rpm.

An underground booster fan installation return connection powered by a cluster of four Aerex type 48G 12v fans forty-eight inches in diameter was also put into use. Nash Hytor pumps were fitted to expel methane gas by means of venturing into the Pollington Smeaton return connection.

During nationalisation production levels reached 750,000 tons per annum with a labour force of 1,420 men.

The colliery was one of the three Yorkshire Government Training Centres used at the time of introduction of the Bevin Boy scheme in 1943.

The colliery closed in December 1992.

Accidents: None are recorded.

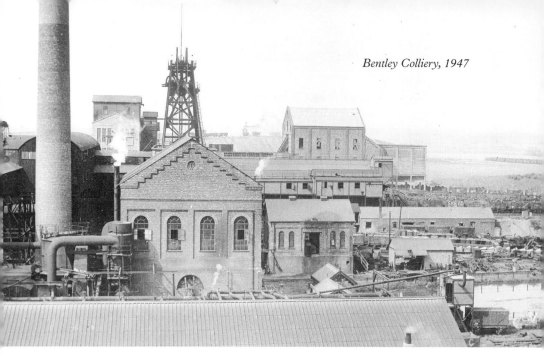

Bentley Colliery, 1947

BENTLEY COLLIERY

Owners: Barber, Walker and Co. Ltd., Bentley, Doncaster.

Location: Bentley.

History: The first sod was cut on 16 March 1905. Coal was reached in May 1907 and the Barnsley seam at a depth of 620 yards in April 1908, after having encountered serious and costly problems from quicksands and an inrush of water while sinking No. 2 shaft using temporary headgear. No. 1 shaft was completed in April 1911.

In September 1931, the river Don burst its banks after heavy rainfall, causing serious flooding to the area surrounding the colliery.

By 1945 the Barnsley and Barnsley Deep seams were being worked with 2,405 men underground and 527 on the surface.

The Dunsil seam was developed in 1940 from the Barnsley level which, in the 1970s, provided the greater part of the output. 1,228 men were producing an annual output of 510,000 tons.

The colliery closed in 1993.

Accidents: On 20 November 1931, an explosion of firedamp caused by gob fire or a safety lamp. The force of the explosion caused serious injuries and burns in addition to the loss of forty-five lives.

Eight miners received the award of the King Edward Medal for their bravery from King George V at Buckingham Palace in February 1933.

BRODSWORTH MAIN COLLIERY

Owners: Doncaster Amalgamated Collieries Ltd. Doncaster, previously known as Brodsworth Main Colliery Co. Ltd.

Location: Pickburn, Doncaster.

History: Brodsworth Main Colliery Company was formed to sink the colliery which was jointly financed by the Staveley Coal and Iron Company and Hickleton Main Colliery Company with capital of £300,000.

The first sod was cut on 23 October 1905, and Nos. 1 and 2 shafts, both twenty-one feet in diameter, were sunk in 1907 to a depth of 601 yards reaching the Barnsley seam.

In 1920 the original two shafts were deepened to 842 yards to the Parkgate seam and in 1923 a third shaft was sunk to the Barnsley seam at a depth of 595 yards. The Parkgate seam closed in October 1927 but reopened in 1935.

The Barnsley seam had been worked continuously throughout the life of the colliery, with the Parkgate seam developed in 1930, the Dunsil seam in 1943 and the Thorncliffe seam in 1948. Mechanised loading at the coalface was introduced in 1953 and a major reconstruction scheme completed in 1961.

No. 1 shaft was equipped with a single cage and balance weight for service duties and No. 2 shaft with a single twenty ton capacity skip

Brodsworth Colliery.

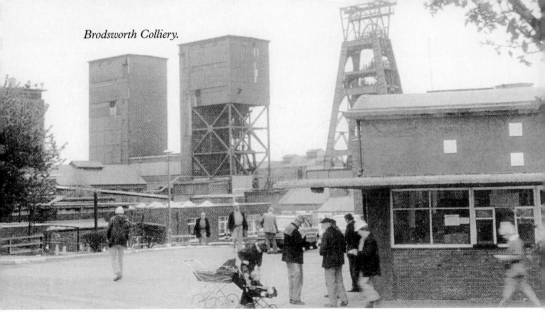

Brodsworth Colliery.

and balance weight for winding coal from the Parkgate and Thorncliffe levels. No. 3 shaft was re-equipped to wind coal from the Barnsley level in two and a half ton mine cars.

All four seams continued working and in 1968 the whole output from the neighbouring Bullcroft colliery was transported underground to Brodsworth for winding. In October 1970 the two collieries fully merged. Bullcroft surface became obsolete.

Coal was carried from the three shafts by belt conveyor to coal preparation screens capable of an output of over 800 tons per hour. At this time production had reached 1,584,000 tons annually with a workforce of 2961 men.

Brodsworth Main closed in 1990.

Accidents: None are recorded.

BULLCROFT MAIN COLLIERY

Owners: Bullcroft Main Collieries, Ltd. later to become part of the Doncaster Amalgamated Collieries Limited.

Location: Carcroft.

History: Bullcroft Colliery Company was formed in April 1908 and sinking began in June of that year. Two shafts were sunk. In January 1909, at a depth of 100 feet, a water feeder yielding 1,000 gallons a minute was struck but successfully controlled. Sinking resumed. However another inrush was encountered at 180 feet. Operations had to be abandoned until powerful electric pumps capable of extracting 6,200 gallons per minute were installed. These proved to be unsuccessful and it was decided to withdraw the pumps and freeze the shafts. This operation commenced in January 1910.

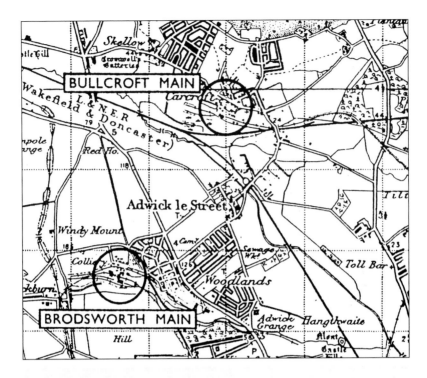

Bullcroft Main Colliery.

The freezing did not entirely come up to expectations but as soon as pumps clearing the shafts stopped, water continued to rise and German workers had to be recalled. In February 1911 iron tubbing was fixed to both shafts. Freezing re-commenced and coal was finally reached.

In 1968, a 550 yard drift was completed linking the Bullcroft and Brodsworth workings. A 1,800 yard long underground conveyor was installed which enabled Bullcroft coal to be wound at Brodsworth.

The collieries merged in September 1970 and the two 684 yards-deep disused shafts were filled in at the end of 1971 using nearby colliery spoil, thereby closing Bullcroft Main in 1970.

Accidents: None are recorded.

DENABY MAIN COLLIERY

Owners: Denaby and Cadeby Main Collieries Ltd. Denaby Main, Rotherham, later to become Amalgamated Denaby Collieries Ltd.

Location: Denaby.

History: The Denaby estate and manor belonged to the Fullerton family of nearby Thrybergh Hall and in July 1863 a lease and partnership was signed between John Fullerton and George Pearson, J B Pope, Richard Pope and Edward Baines junior, each of whom had partnerships in either Darfield Main, Crigglestone Cliffe and New Sharlston collieries.

Denaby Main is situated about six miles from Doncaster. The sinking of the shaft commenced immediately in 1863 when a gamble was taken to sink for coal beneath magnesium limestone rock, in spite of opposition from mining engineers who contended that there

Denaby Main Colliery, 1914.

Denaby Main Colliery, 1962.

Denaby miners' houses in 1975. Note the television aerials and the slag heap.

Denaby Main Colliery, 1965.

were no further reserves of coal. However, despite this, the geologists were correct in their original contention that coal did exist under the formation.

A large amount of water was encountered during the shaft sinking and the Barnsley seam was reached in September 1867 at a depth of 422 yards.

In 1868 it was decided to form a limited company with Sir Edward Baines, MP for Leeds, as chairman, who took over his son's share on his death, and Richard Pope as managing director. At the same time a colliery manager was appointed at a salary of £150 a year plus a free house.

The colliery was not without its share of disputes. On at least three occasions conflict between miners and employers resulted in eviction from company cottages. The disputes were finally resolved in September 1869 when the colliery company agreed to employ union men.

It soon became apparent that houses, schools, churches, medical and social facilities were needed to cope with an increase in the population and in 1892 new terraced type houses were built for the miners close to the pit. The density of housing was forty to the acre, compared with the ten to fourteen per acre allowed today.

Electric lighting was installed at the colliery and a passenger station was opened at Denaby by the South Yorkshire Junction Railway in 1894. The station closed in 1927.

The colliery continued to prosper and the workforce was increased by 250 men in 1869 to 5,142 (combined with Cadeby) in 1911. The colliery changed its name to Amalgamated Denaby Collieries Limited in May 1936.

The colliery closed in 1968.

Accidents: None are recorded.

FRICKLEY COLLIERY

Owners: Carlton Main Colliery Co. Ltd. Barnsley.

Location: South Elmsall.

History: The mine was sunk between 1903 and 1905 to work the Barnsley seam at a depth of 664 yards.

Manpower figures are as follows:

1910 - 1,463 underground - 276 surface.

1927 - A total of 3,400 men working the Barnsley, Shafton and Parkgate seams.

1945 - 2,232 underground - 518 surface. Barnsley and Barnsley Deep.

The Frickley colliery was closed in 1993.

Frickley Colliery, c.1905.

Frickley Colliery, c.1925.

SOUTH ELMSALL COLLIERY
Owners: Carlton Main Colliery Co. Ltd. Barnsley.
Location: South Elmsall.
History: Sunk in 1923 to work the Cudworth seam.
Manpower figures as follows:
1945 - 124 undergound - ten surface. Shafton seam.
The two pits shared common services and were combined during the period of NCB control.
The colliery at South Elmsall closed in 1968.
Accidents: None are recorded at either colliery.

GOLDTHORPE COLLIERY
Owners: Goldthorpe Collieries Ltd. Dodworth. Barnsley.
Location: Goldthorpe.
History: The mine was sunk to work the Shafton seam at a depth of sixty-five yards in 1910.
Manpower figures as follows:
1927 - 276 underground - fifty-three surface working the Shafton seam.

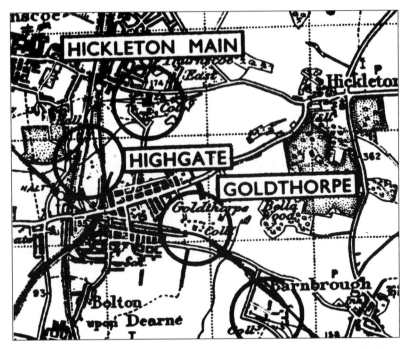

1945 - 268 underground - eighty surface working the Shafton seam.

Coal production ceased in February 1994, in spite of the high production of coal for the power station market.

Northern Group director, Alan Houghton, issued a statement at that time: *'I have nothing but praise for the management and workforce at Goldthorpe as their performances have been the most consistent of any mine within British Coal.'*

HIGHGATE COLLIERY

Owners: Highgate Colliery Co. (1943) Ltd. Goldthorpe, Rotherham.

Location: Goldthorpe.

History: The mine was sunk to work the Shafton seam at a depth of fifty yards in 1916.

Manpower figures were as follows:

1927 - 148 underground - thirty-four surface working the Shafton seam.

1945 - 159 underground - sixty-six surface working the Shafton seam.

In 1958 shaft coal winding was replaced by a 2,000 yard drift mine sloping from the surface, and this was also used to convey output from Highgate Colliery workings direct to the surface. The shafts were replaced by drift mines in 1948. These were used until 1966 when the underground connection enabled output to surface at Goldthorpe Colliery. The two pits thus combined as Goldthorpe/Highgate Colliery when 1,340 men produced an annual output of 834,000 tons.

The combined colliery closed in 1994.

Accidents: None are recorded.

HATFIELD MAIN COLLIERY

Owners: Hatfield Main Colliery Co. Ltd. Stainforth, Doncaster.
Location: Stainforth.
History: The first sod was cut in October 1911 and sinking began in the November of that year. Coal was reached on 12 May 1916, and the Barnsley bed on 14 August at a depth of 857 yards.

Permanent head stocks and winding engines were installed in 1915.

In 1927 the Barnsley and Kents Thick seams were worked and during 1945 the Barnsley seam was still being worked in addition to the High Hazel seam.

During the 1970s an annual output of 655,000 tons was produced using a total manpower of 1,712 men.

The colliery closed in 1993.

Accidents: None are recorded.

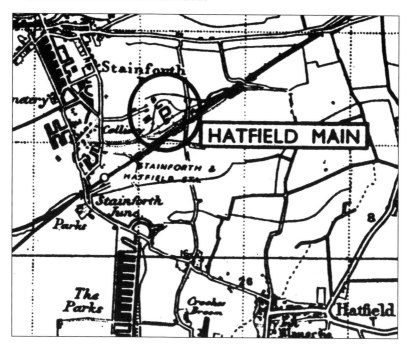

Hatfield Main Colliery, Stainforth, c. 1920.

Hatfield Main Colliery, Stainforth.

HICKLETON MAIN COLLIERY

Owners: Doncaster Amalgamated Collieries Ltd, Doncaster. Previously Hickleton Main Colliery Co. Ltd.

Location: Thurnscoe, Rotherham.

History: The pit was sunk during the strike of 1893 by the owners, Messrs. Eaton and Walker, and reached to the Barnsley seam at a depth of 540 yards in 1894.

Hickleton Main had a good reputation for being a safe pit, mainly due to efficient management. In 1911 the colliery broke the world's record for raising the greatest tonnage of coal.

In 1921 one of the original shafts was deepened and a new shaft sunk to the Parkgate seam at 789 yards.

During 1945 the Barnsley, Barnsley Deep, Low Main and Parkgate seams were being worked.

Accidents: At 5.00 pm on 24-25 October 1922, Arthur Bridges was completely buried by a heavy roof fall caused by the gob, or empty space, created with the removal of the coal seam, which knocked out the timber supports. His workmates worked unceasingly to free him despite being hampered by continuous roof falls. Finally, at 10.30 am the following day, he was freed, still alive.

Although he only suffered bruises to his legs, he died seven hours

Hickleton Main Subscription, silver prize band, 1923.

later as the result of shock after being buried for seventeen and a half hours.

The bravery of the four rescuers was recognised by each being awarded the coveted King Edward Medal.

The colliery closed in 1986.

MARKHAM MAIN COLLIERY

Owners: Doncaster Amalgamated Collieries Ltd., Doncaster.

Location: Armthorpe, Doncaster.

History: In June 1913 the lease of the mineral rights were secured from Lord Fitzwilliam by Sir Arthur Markham. Sinking was to begin immediately by the International Boring Company using German labour.

The operations ceased at the outbreak of war and it was not until 5 May 1924 that the shafts finally reached the Barnsley seam at a depth of 730 yards.

Figures for 1945 show that 2,272 men worked underground and 360 on the surface working the Barnsley seam.

During nationalisation in the 1970s a total of 1,500 men produced an annual output of 650,000 tons.

The colliery closed in 1992.

Accidents: None are recorded.

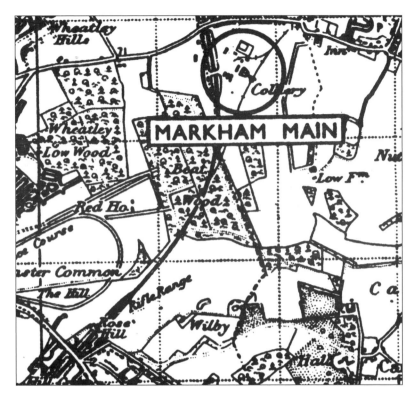

ROSSINGTON MAIN COLLIERY

Owners: Amalgamated Denaby Collieries Ltd., Doncaster.

Location: Rossington, Doncaster.

History: The colliery was originally owned by the Sheepbridge and John Brown and Company.

The twenty-two feet diameter No. 1 shaft was started on 10 July 1912 and reached the Barnsley seam at a depth of 872 yards on 3 May 1915. Sinking continued to the Dunsil seam at a depth of 888 yards. Considerable water problems were encountered during the operation at the rate of 1,800 to 2,100 gallons per hour.

No. 2 shaft was sunk on 26 June 1912, and reached the Barnsley seam on 7 November 1915. The Dunsil seam was reached on 18 November 1915.

Coal winding started on 17 July 1916, and 107,800 tons were wound during that first year.

The pit continued to prosper and by 1937 the tonnage raised was 1,009,815.

In 1953 a major reconstruction scheme was started replacing

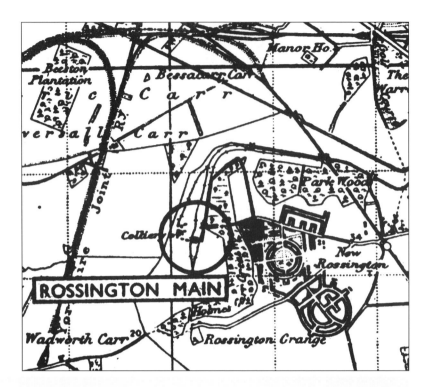

Rossington Main Colliery

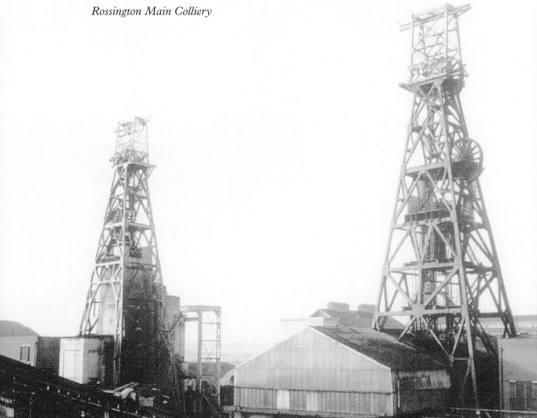

endless rope haulages with diesel locomotives. No. 1 and No. 2 shafts were deepened to the Swallow Wood seam in 1964 to a depth of 928 yards. Skip winding was installed using twelve ton capacity skips in No. 2 shaft.

Powered supports were introduced in September 1965 and coal production ceased in the Dunsil seam on 18 October 1968. New electric fans were installed on the surface replacing the old 900 hp steam powered fans.

Methane gas was used to fire the boilers at the colliery. Rapid loading facilities were completed in 1971 and the colliery produced an annual output of 903,000 tons with a workforce of 1,681 men.

The colliery closed in 1993 and reopened by R J B Mining in 1994.

Accidents: None are recorded.

THORNE COLLIERY

Owners: Pease and Partners Ltd.

Location: Thorne.

History: Sinking began on 12 October 1909, but was suspended in July 1910 until powerful electric pumps had been installed to deal with an inflow of water of 9,000 gallons per minute. A month later sinking resumed, but again stopped in December 1911 until a German freezing process could be implemented to deal with the water problem in August 1912.

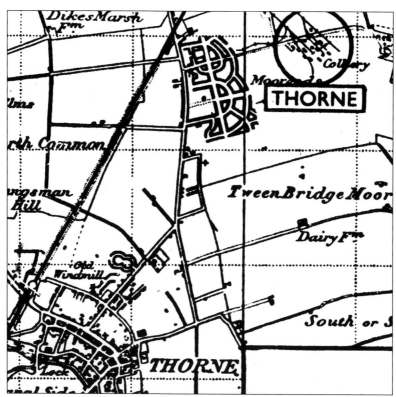

Thorne Colliery, c.1926

The outbreak of the war put an end to the German Freezing Company and it was not until after the war that the François Cementation process could be used. However water problems continued as the pumps were not adequate to cope with the flooding.

New Sulzer Centrifugal pumps arrived at the end of 1919 when sinking continued and it was not until July 1922 that No. 1 shaft finally reached a depth of 346 yards before striking solid limestone. The difficulties had been considerable as pump motors burnt out and shafts continually filled with water.

No. 2 shaft was left standing until 17 August 1922, when pumping re-commenced. Freezing boreholes were even more troublesome than in No. 1 shaft and it was not until 31 May 1924, that solid limestone was reached at a depth of 345 yards. Sinking continued to a depth of 964 yards and was completed on 13 March 1926, seventeen years after commencement of the operation. The seams mined were the Barnsley and High Hazel. Thorne was the deepest colliery in Yorkshire.

The colliery closed in 1956.

Accidents: On 15 March 1926, breakdown of a capstan engine caused scaffolding to sink in the shaft with the loss of six lives.

YORKSHIRE MAIN COLLIERY

Owners: Doncaster Amalgamated Collieries Ltd., Doncaster.
Location: Edlington.
History: Two shafts were sunk between December 1909 and July 1911 to a depth of 905 yards when the colliery started production. The colliery at that time was owned by the Staveley Coal Co. Ltd of Edlington and was then known as Edlington Colliery.

As development took place, the shafts were found to lie in a heavily faulted area, which made the pit bottom below the level of the major reserves of coal in the Barnsley seam.

The original method of working was by longwall faces, divided into 'tub stalls', the coal being hand filled into tubs on the coal face.

In 1933 the 'tub stalls' system was replaced by the method of longwall advancing coal faces with conveyors and a central roadway conveyor to transport the coal to a loading point on the main roadway in settled ground behind the working face.

A scheme for the reconstruction of Yorkshire Main was considered by Doncaster Amalgamated Collieries Limited, and was adopted by the National Coal Board at the time of take over.

It was planned to introduce underground locomotive haulage using large capacity mine cars, install skip winding plant at No. 2 shaft and a subsidiary mine car winding plant at the No. 1 shaft. The locomotive haulage necessitated the construction of a new pit bottom approximately sixty yards above the old level and the driving

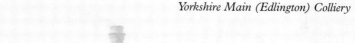

Yorkshire Main (Edlington) Colliery

of connecting roadways to the new level. The changes in the winding plant entailed alterations to the surface coal handling equipment between the top of the shaft and coal preparation plant.

The erection of the skip winding equipment began early in 1952 and was completed by January 1953, with the gradual introduction of mine cars by July 1953.

While there still was a considerable amount of work to be completed, the priority was to erect a plant to clarify the water used in the coal cleaning process and then build an additional washery with a capacity of 100 to 150 tons an hour to deal with the increased output.

The net capital investment in the colliery since nationalisation amounted to £1,215,408.

The seams worked at that time were the Barnsley and Dunsil which had a projected life expectancy of seventy years.

During 1910, at the time of sinking of the shafts, 182 men worked underground with only seventy-five on the surface, but by 1945 2,118 worked underground and 474 were employed on the surface.

In 1922 the pit owners provided the village of Edlington with an open air swimming pool.

In the 1970s 1,783 men produced an annual output of 705,000 tons worked from the Barnsley seam, which produced most of the output, and the Swallow Wood seam.

The colliery closed in 1985.

Accidents: None are recorded.

CHAPTER TEN

The Collieries of South Yorkshire

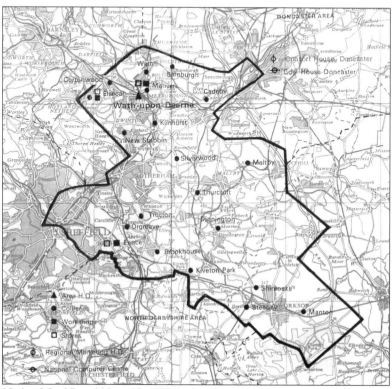

National Coal Board Map of South Yorkshire Area Collieries (1971). HM Stationery Office.

BARNBURGH MAIN COLLIERY previously known as BARNBOROUGH COLLIERY

Owners of Barnborough Colliery were Manvers Main Collieries Ltd. but later became Barnburgh Colliery under the control of the National Coal Board.

Location: Barnburgh.

History: Approximately one and a half miles from the Goldthorpe Colliery, the shafts were first sunk between 1912 and 1915 to the Parkgate seam which was reached in 1914 and,

Barnborough Main colliery, 1913.

Barnborough Main colliery, 1953.

Barnborough Main colliery, 1958.

Barnborough Main colliery, 1961.

together with the Barnsley seam, yielded coal until 1938.

The first face conveyor was opened in 1935 and skip winding introduced in 1937.

A new winding engine was installed at No. 6 shaft, which was in fact American made and had been destined for Russia. It was powered by two 1,305 kw motors.

The period between 1950 and 1956 saw major reconstruction at Barnburgh involving the construction of a new pit bottom at the Winter seam horizon, the winding of all coal from three levels up the one shaft and the overland rail transportation of coal to Manvers.

Before its closure in 1989 coal was being mined from three fully mechanised faces in the Meltonfield seam with a workforce of 1,200 men producing over half a million tons annually.

Accidents: On 24 April 1942, a floor upheaval caused by a rock bump in the Parkgate seam imprisoned thirteen miners.

Without any warning the floor of open roads suddenly lifted to the roof, completely sealing off any passage. The shock wave caused considerable devastation in the district reducing a twelve foot roadway eight feet high, supported by steel arches, to become buckled and twisted. The discharge of a large quantity of firedamp added to the dangers of the situation.

After forty-two hours sufficient debris had been removed to enable eight men to be rescued relatively uninjured. The following day nine more men were reached, only five of whom had survived.

On 26 June 1957, a flash from a damaged electric cable resulted in an ignition of a firedamp explosion, causing the loss of six lives.

The colliery closed in 1989.

BROOKHOUSE COLLIERY
Owners: Sheffield Coal Co. Ltd
Location: Beighton
History: The colliery opened in 1902 and was situated about seven miles south-east of Sheffield. Originally it was known as Beighton Brookhouse.

Between 1929 and 1930, in what had become known as Brookhouse Colliery, two circular shafts, each eighteen feet in diameter, were sunk about three quarters of a mile apart.

The Beighton shaft, which would have been coupled with the old Birley (Beighton Pit), was the upcast and 1,282 feet deep to the lowest entrance at the Silkstone seam and was used for carrying materials and a small number of men between shifts. This shaft also served as the ventilation shaft for supplying air to Brookhouse. In 1942 all coal was transferred to the new Brookhouse shaft which became the main access into the mine.

During the period of nationalisation new skip winding installations were introduced at the time when the Thorncliffe seam was being worked producing an annual output of 299,054 tons with a work force of 757 miners.

Birley East Pit became one of the three Yorkshire Government Training Centre Pits, used for training Bevin Boys during the Second World War.

The colliery closed in 1985.

Accidents: On 4 March 1958, in the No. 1 downcast shaft, thirty-six miners were injured in a shaft overwind accident caused by the excessive speed of a winding engine with faulty brakes.

CADEBY MAIN COLLIERY
Owners: Amalgamated Denaby Collieries Ltd. Doncaster.
Location: Cadeby.
History: Cadeby Main was sunk in 1889 to the Barnsley seam.

This colliery was originally owned by the Denaby and Cadeby Main Collieries Ltd. who also owned Denaby Main Colliery.

The freak of nature which formed the Southerly Don Fault has enabled the combined output of two merged collieries, Denaby and

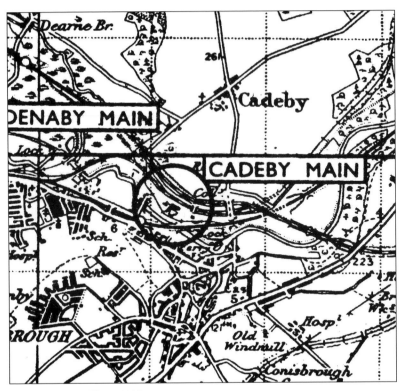

Cadeby Main colliery, 1909.

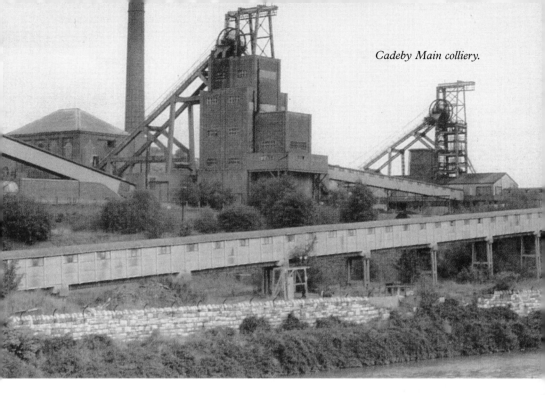

Cadeby Main colliery.

Cadeby to be wound at Cadeby since 1956. This fault diverts the Barnsley seam, worked from Cadeby until its exhaustion in 1966, almost parallel to the Beamshaw seam where a series of cross-measure drifts linked the two collieries until their merger in March 1968.

The Barnsley seam provided the bulk of Cadeby's output since its sinking and the shallower Beamshaw and deeper Dunsil were developed in the later years to make up the overall output.

Exploratory workings were undertaken in the Swallow Wood seam in the pit's early years, but it was not until 1960 that this seam was finally developed. Two faces in this seam provided 40 per cent of the annual output, but the remainder came from the two faces in the Dunsil seam. All faces were fully mechanised and equipped with powered roof supports.

During the 1970s the colliery employed 1,180 men producing over 400,000 tons annually.

The colliery closed in 1986.

Accidents: On 9 July 1912, two explosions of firedamp and coal dust ignited by gob-fire occurred. The first explosion happened on the night shift between 10.00 pm and 6.00 am and killed thirty-five men.

The second explosion, between 10.30 am and 11.00 am, claimed the lives of fifty-three men engaged in the rescue operation following the first explosion.

The combined death toll of those directly killed in the accident was eighty-eight men, which included three HM Inspectors of Mines and the managers of both Cadeby and Denaby Main collieries.

A miraculous coincidence saved many lives. King George V and Queen Mary paid a royal visit to Conisbrough Castle. Many miners had taken a shift off work to watch. Because of this only 111 men were at work underground on that occasion. 489 men had been working the corresponding shift the previous week and 505 on the night shift.

Fifty-four of those killed were residents of Denaby. Many of those who survived were left in a traumatised state. One, James Burns, lost the mouthpiece of his breathing apparatus, his jaws became locked and, despite being assisted by two men at the time, found it impossible to unlock his jaws for oxygen to be administered and consequently died.

A second victim, Frank Wood, who had been involved in the task of removing bodies, committed suicide by drowning himself in the River Don.

A third victim, bringing the eventual total to ninety-one, was James Springthorpe, a colliery deputy who had a miraculous escape from the original explosions died from the effects on 25 March 1913.

The last of the bodies of the victims was finally retrieved from the pit in September, two months after the disaster.

The Home Office Report on the Cadeby explosions highlighted questions of putting coal production and profit before safety preventative measures. Statements between W H Chambers, managing director of Denaby and Cadeby Main Collieries and Herbert Smith, president of the Yorkshire Miners' Association made this very evident.

CORTONWOOD COLLIERY

Owners: Cortonwood Collieries Co. Ltd., Wombwell, Barnsley; previously at West Melton, Rotherham.

Location: Wombwell.

History: One of South Yorkshire's old collieries dating back to 1873 when a shaft was sunk to a depth of 210 yards to the Barnsley seam. The shafts were subsequently deepened to the Thorncliffe seam between 1907 and 1908 and further deepened to 574 yards intersecting the Silkstone seam in 1925. Three of the four seams were successfully worked until

Cortonwood Colliery, 1984.

exhausted - the Barnsley in 1921, the Parkgate in 1941 and the Swallow Wood in 1975. The Silkstone seam was developed in 1927 and became the colliery's main source of supply until closure.

A big reconstruction scheme initiated by the NCB was undertaken, which took eight years to complete, and involved a concentration of coal winding skips in No. 1 shaft, installation of electric winding engines, compressors, coal preparation plant and underground reorganisation of the trunk conveyor system.

Before its closure in 1985 the colliery was producing over 326,000 tons annually with 800 men.

Accidents: On 8 December 1932, seven miners were killed in an explosion of fire damp caused by shot-firing.

Again, on 19 June 1961, four miners died from suffocation from an outburst of firedamp caused by floor upheaval.

Dinnington Main Colliery, 1909.

DINNINGTON MAIN COLLIERY

    Owners: Amalgamated Denaby Collieries Ltd, Doncaster, previously Dinnington Main Coal Co. Ltd.

    Location: Dinnington.

    History: Dinnington Colliery was located twelve miles east of

Dinnington Main Colliery.

Sheffield and eight miles north-west of Worksop and was first sunk between 1903 and 1905 to a depth of 666 yards to reach the Barnsley seam. This seam provided the bulk of the colliery's output over the years and in 1960 a large scale reorganisation was started to concentrate workings in the north-east area of the seam.

Seven years later, in 1967, another seam was developed to replace the declining Barnsley production. The Swallow Wood seam, lying eighty yards below Barnsley, was reached by driving two inclined tunnels from the Barnsley workings. And then, in 1971, the Haigh Moor seam was developed as the Barnsley seam became exhausted.

Dinnington was in the forefront of coalface mechanisation from the late 1940s when a limited use of power loading was introduced. In 1964 all faces at the colliery were power loaded followed by the installation of powered roof supports on all faces. In 1974, further modernisation included skip winding, new coal preparation plant and electrification of winders.

During the 1970s the colliery was producing an annual output of 308,840 tons with a workforce of 991 men.

The colliery closed in 1991.

Accidents: None are recorded.

ELSECAR COLLIERY

Owners: Earl Fitzwilliam Collieries Co., Elsecar.

Situated: Elsecar, between Barnsley and Rotherham.

History: The early history of the Elsecar Collieries is shown in the list below.

Year	Collieries	Names	Employees
1795	4	Elsecar, 'Old' and 'New' Lawwood and Westwood	79
1819	5	Elsecar, 'Old' and 'New' Haugh, Lawwood and Brampton	197
1828	6	Elsecar, 'Old' and 'New' Rainber Park, Swallow Wood & Parkgate	317
1845	6	Elsecar, 'High', 'Middle' & 'Low' (Hemingfield), Strafford Main, Parkgate & Kents Main.	587
1856	7	Elsecar, Parkgate Collieries, Strafford Main.	869

Elsecar Main Colliery, 1917.

It was not until between 1905 and 1908 that proper coal extraction began under the Earl Fitzwilliam Collieries Co. when shafts were sunk to work the Parkgate seam at a depth of 364 yards. In 1925 the No. 1 shaft was extended to 534 yards to reach the Silkstone seam which was worked in 1927, where the first electrical coal cutter and the first compressed air shaker pans were used on the faces.

Subsequent developments in the Thorncliffe and Swallow Wood seams took place in 1938 and 1945 respectively. The Swallow Wood seam output was conveyed to the surface via a one-in-five gradient drift, driven in 1945. The Parkgate seam was exhausted in 1961, the Thorncliffe seam in 1972 and the Silkstone seam in 1975.

The colliery output during the 1970s reached 360,000 tons a year from the Swallow Wood and a newly developed Lidgett, which replaced the worked out Thorncliffe seam in 1972.

During 1910 Elsecar Main employed 644 men underground and 117 on the surface working the Parkgate seam whilst at nearby Hemingfield there were 310 underground and forty-six men on the surface working the Barnsley seam. By 1927 Elsecar Main was employing 1,550 men underground and 350 on the surface.

During 1945, prior to nationalisation Elsecar Main was employing 1,305 underground and 472 on the surface whilst Elsecar and Hemingfield were pumping stations under the control of the South Yorkshire Mines Drainage Committee.

The colliery closed in 1983.

Accidents: On 22 December 1852, ten miners were killed in an explosion of firedamp caused by a naked flame.

THE NEWCOMEN ENGINE AT ELSECAR

Elsecar has fortunately been preserved as a conservation area. It is a living museum depicting the time of the Industrial Revolution. The attractions include industrial workshops originally owned by the Earls Fitzwilliam, restored buildings and monuments from the time of the Industrial Revolution. Close by is the Elsecar branch of the Dearne and Dove canal, as well as a preserved steam railway from Rockingham station to the Hemingfield basin on the canal.

The star exhibit is the Newcomen engine. Originally an atmospheric engine was built to pump water out of Earl Fitzwilliam's new colliery at Elsecar in September 1795, coinciding with the cutting of the Elsecar branch of the Dearne and Dove Canal.

The Newcomen-type engine designed after Thomas Newcomen was built at the end of the eighteenth century and operated continually for a century and a quarter until 1923, when it was replaced by more modern equipment. However, five years later it was brought back into service to replace electric pumps which were put out of action through flooding.

The sinking of the engine pit began in the summer of 1794 and the construction of the engine house later that year. The whole project was completed a year later. Engine parts from Chambers and

Elsecar Newcomen Engine, 1983.

Newton (later Newton and Chambers) of Thorncliffe were subsequently ordered.

In 1799 the pump shaft broke and the colliery was flooded. This prompted its replacement by a larger new cylinder and in 1811 the beam of the great engine needed replacement.

In 1812 the Elsecar Engine could draw forty gallons at one stroke and was capable of thirteen strokes per minute to draw 748,800 gallons of water every twenty-four hours, but the engine only worked twelve hours a day.

By 1836 it was reported by Benjamin Biram, who was steward of the Fitzwilliam household and collieries, that the wooden beam was cracked and the three pumps were corroded. The wooden beam needed to be replaced by a cast iron one for the great engine.

It is the only engine of its type in the world and remains intact as a monument to the past industrial age for all to see.

KILNHURST COLLIERY

Owners: Manvers Main Collieries. Wath-upon-Dearne, Rotherham. Kilnhurst was originally owned by J and J Charlesworth in the early 1920s and was coupled with Swinton Common colliery. A take over by Stewarts and Lloyds from J and J Charlesworth in December 1924 was followed by a purchase by the Tinsley Park Colliery Company in June 1936.

Location: Kilnhurst

History: Kilnhurst, situated three miles from Rotherham, is one of four collieries constructed between 1950 and 1956 forming the

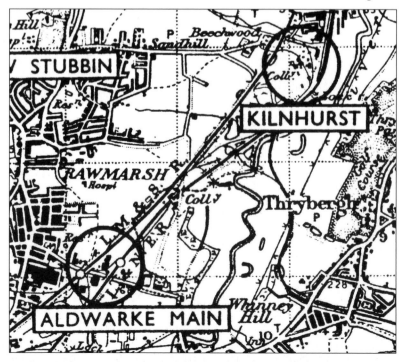

Kilnhurst Colliery, 1960.

Kilnhurst Colliery, 1969.

£6¹/₂ million Manvers Central Scheme to enable their combined outputs to be transported either on the surface or underground to a central plant at Manvers. The scheme would drastically reduce the cost of expensive coal preparation plants and equipment at four individual collieries.

The colliery was originally sunk in 1858 and covered a workable area of nearly four square miles bounded by Southerly and Northerly Don Faults and contains the long abandoned Barnsley, High Hazel and Silkstone seams. The Parkgate seam was abandoned in 1966.

During the 1960s coal was mined from two fully mechanised faces in the Swallow Wood seam which was abandoned in 1944, but subsequently redeveloped in 1952.

During the period of reconstruction in the middle 1950s coal ceased to be wound but transported by diesel locomotives to be wound at Manvers.

During this period the colliery was producing over 2,000,000 tons annually with a workforce of 596 men.

The colliery closed in l986.

Accidents: None are recorded.

KIVETON PARK

Owners: Kiveton Park Coal Co. Ltd. Sheffield.

Location: Kiveton Park.

History: Sunk in 1866 to the Barnsley seam and deepened to the Thorncliffe at 669 yards in 1884, the colliery was situated just inside the southern boundary of the South Yorkshire Area nine miles from Sheffield.

An extensive development scheme completed in 1977 opened up the Clowne seam which extended the life of the colliery for more than twenty years. The scheme replaced the capacities in the Barnsley and High Hazel seams, the former being worked out and the latter severely disturbed geologically.

A major £1 million modernisation scheme was completed in 1964 which included the erection of a new coal preparation plant, installation of new electric winders in both shafts, new pit bank and headgear at No. 1 shaft and a new ventilation fan.

The output at that time was in the region of 490,000 tons annually won from three Clowne faces equipped with powered roof supports.

A new drift from the surface to Clowne seam was started in 1974 and completed in 1977, the drift being used for manriding and materials haulage as well as having a cable belt for transporting mineral.

Accidents: None are recorded.

MALTBY MAIN COLLIERY

Owners: Amalgamated Denaby Collieries Ltd, Doncaster, previously Maltby Main Colliery Co. Ltd.

Location: Maltby near Rotherham.

History: Originally sunk between 1907 and 1911 to the Barnsley seam at a depth of 820 yards.

The colliery is situated six miles to the east of Rotherham and has a history of high methane gas emission and therefore was one of the first collieries

Maltby Main Colliery.

in Yorkshire to adopt a methane drainage system.

A massive fourteen year reconstruction programme was completed in 1961 which made the colliery into one of the largest in Yorkshire. Part of the scheme included a new pit bottom and service roadways, new electric winders, a new coal preparation plant and ventilation fan and the introduction of battery locomotive haulage underground.

A further extensive £1.25 million development started in 1968 and completed in 1971 gave the pit another fifty years of life to provide extra coal for the important coking market.

At that time the colliery was producing 900,000 tons annually employing 1,400 men, using the latest coalface and ancillary equipment to mechanically cut and load coal for the coking, power station, industrial and house coal markets.

The colliery today is operated by R J B Mining and is currently producing 3,346 tons per day.

Accidents: On 28 July 1923, ignition by spontaneous combustion caused an explosion of firedamp costing the lives of twenty-seven miners.

MANVERS MAIN COLLIERY

Owners: Manvers Main Collieries Ltd, Wath-upon-Dearne, Rotherham.

Location: Wath-upon-Dearne.

History: Located midway between Wath, Swinton, Mexborough and Bolton-upon-Dearne, the first shaft was sunk in 1868 to the

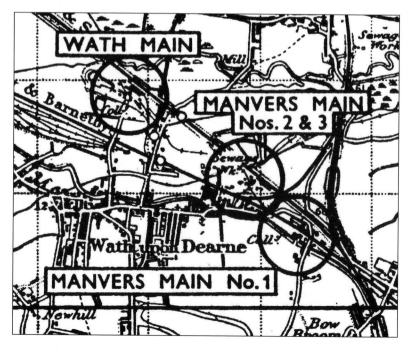

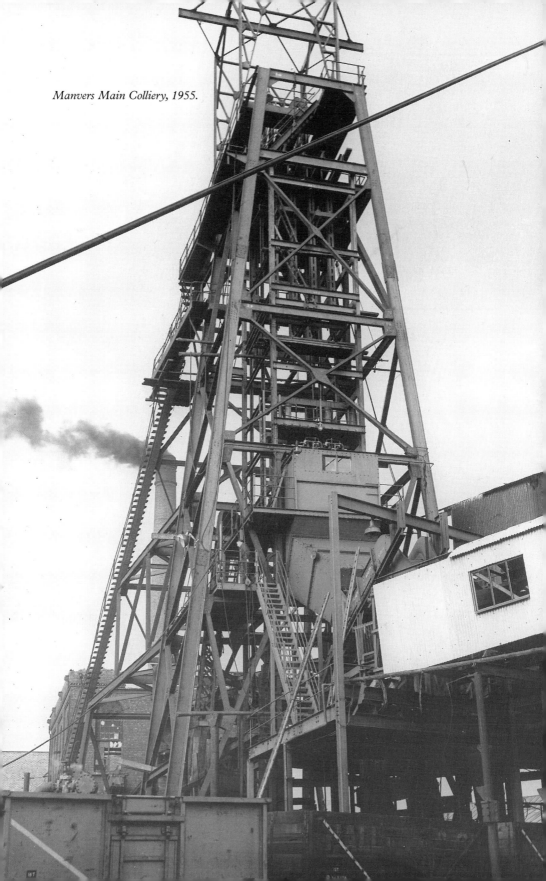

Manvers Main Colliery, 1955.

Manvers Main Colliery, 1962.

Manvers Main Colliery, 1962.

Barnsley seam at a depth of 281 yards. Additional shaft sinking took place between 1877 and 1901 to work the Parkgate and Swallow Wood seams and in later years the Meltonfield and Silkstone seams.

Manvers is one of four collieries reconstructed between 1950 and 1956 forming the £6.5 million Manvers Central which enables the combined outputs to be transported either on the surface or underground to a central coal preparation plant.

The principal features of the scheme were to concentrate the coal winding at Manvers, the Manvers Swallow Wood seam and nearby Wath collieries' outputs being wound up No. 2 shaft while the remaining Manvers output, plus that from Kilnhurst Colliery, wound up No. 3 shaft.

Diesel locomotives were to be used to transport the two supplying collieries' outputs through linking roadways to the Manvers pit bottom. Output during nationalisation was 450,000 tons annually mined from fully mechanised coalfaces in the Silkstone and Swallow Wood seams. The high quality coking coal production employed over 1,300 miners.

The colliery closed in 1988.

Accidents: On 4 March 1945, five men were killed by an explosion caused by an ignition of firedamp by a damaged trailing cable of a Joy loader.

NEW STUBBIN COLLIERY

Owners: Earl Fitzwilliam Collieries Co., Elsecar, Barnsley.

Location: Elsecar.

History: New Stubbin Colliery is a new colliery compared to the majority of century old pits in South Yorkshire.

Sunk between 1915 and 1916 to the 278 yards deep Parkgate seam which provided total output until the Thorncliffe seam was developed in 1933. A new canteen was opened by Earl Fitzwilliam in May 1934. Lady Fitzwilliam opened the New Stubbin Colliery miners' restaurant in November 1941. The colliery was reconstructed between 1953 and 1955, the main features being the deepening of the shafts to develop the Silkstone seam at 421 yards, the complete electrification of the colliery and the construction of a new coal preparation plant.

During this period the colliery's annual output was 420,000 tons produced from the Thorncliffe and Silkstone seams. The Parkgate seam became exhausted after fifty years of continuous working.

The Thorncliffe output was transferred by spiral chute to the Silkstone horizon and then hauled to the pit bottom by diesel locomotives. 800 men were employed.

New Stubbin was fast reaching the end of coal reserves in February 1977 after 100 years of mining. It was estimated that 20 million tons of coal had been produced since 1919. The colliery closed in 1978.

Accidents: None are recorded.

NUNNERY COLLIERY

Owners: Nunnery Colliery Co. Ltd. Sheffield.

Location: Handsworth.

History: The mine was originally sunk in 1868 and worked by the owner of the property, the Duke of Norfolk, until 1874 when it was acquired by the Nunnery Colliery Co. Ltd., who worked the Parkgate and Silkstone seams.

The head office of the company was situated in the Exchange buildings in Sheffield with a handsomely furnished board room, private rooms for the heads of several departments together with well appointed general offices for the numerous clerical staff employed.

One half of all the house coal consumed in Sheffield came from the Nunnery colliery.

The colliery produced the finest washed steel melting coke, amounting to a daily output of over 200 tons.

The company laid down a large plant capable of washing 1,000 tons of slack and nuts per day in the early 1900s.

The colliery continued to produce coal for ninety-five years and by the 1950s coal supplies rapidly exhausted leading to its closure in 1953.

Accidents: On 3 December 1923, an underground accident caused by a haulage rope breaking cost the lives of seven miners.

ORGREAVE COLLIERY

Owners: United Steel Companies. Treeton, Rotherham. Previously known as Rothervale Collieries Ltd.

Location: Treeton.

History: Situated between Sheffield and Rotherham this was the oldest working colliery in South Yorkshire.

Orgreave colliery, originally known as Dore House colliery, began in 1795. It was re-opened in 1851 when two shafts were sunk to the Barnsley seam. The colliery was in full production by 1860 using the pillar and stall system.

The shafts were deepened to the Silkstone seam between 1887 and 1890, passing through the Haigh Moor seam, the Flockton seam

Orgreave Colliery, 1977.

Orgreave Colliery, 1969.

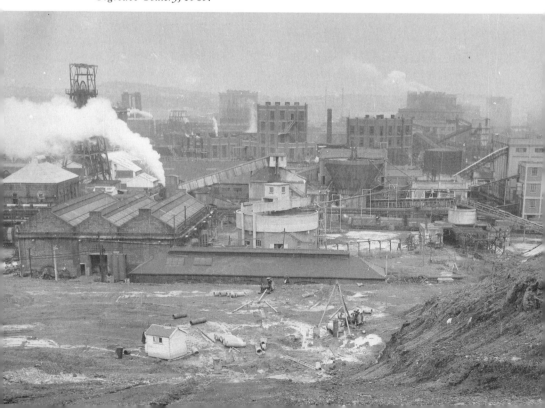

Orgreave Colliery, 1974.

and the Parkgate seam. The Silkstone seam finished production in
1965 and the Parkgate in 1962.

The haulage of the tubs of twelve cwt. capacity was conveyed by
the endless rope method known as lashing. The coal was wound out
of the Parkgate Shaft in a four decked cage, two tubs to each deck,
at the rate of sixty pulls an hour, with a payload of about five tons a
pull.

A century saw many changes at the mine with the introduction of
mechanisation, large and well ventilated airways, underground
lighting and man-riding haulages to and from the coal faces.

No. 1 shaft was the downcast with air being circulated by a
powerful electric fan at the rate of about 200,000 cubic feet per
minute and being drawn up the upcast No. 2 shaft.

The depths of the shafts were: Barnsley seam, 132 yards, Haigh
Moor seam, 202 yards, Flockton seam, 328 yards, Parkgate seam,
386 yards and Silkstone seam, 404 yards.

The colliery had an underground connection to Treeton colliery in the Swallow Wood seam and was sealed off at the Treeton end when the colliery closed.

In the years before closure in 1981 the labour force was just under 1,000 and the average weekly output was 10,000 tons.

The colliery was closed in October 1981.

Accidents: None are recorded.

SILVERWOOD COLLIERY

Owners: Dalton Main Collieries Ltd. Rotherham.

Location: Thrybergh, near Rotherham.

History: Silverwood Colliery is situated three miles east-north-east of Rotherham.

The sinking of the two shafts commenced in April 1900 with the East Pit reaching the Barnsley seam at a depth of 740 yards in 1903, and coal winding commenced at the West Pit in 1905.

Coal headings were driven from the adjacent Roundwood Colliery workings to Silverwood in readiness for the shaft sinking connection, so that the Roundwood coal could be wound at Silverwood.

The Barnsley Seam provided the total output of the mine until 1953. Maximum gross output was achieved in 1929, when 1,322,501

Silverwood Colliery.

Silverwood Colliery, 1963.

Silverwood Colliery, 1955.

Silverwood Colliery, 1958.

Silverwood Colliery.

tons were drawn from both shafts. The Roundwood Colliery ceased coal production in June 1931 due to output quota restrictions.

A major reconstruction scheme was undertaken at Silverwood between 1953 and 1962, the main features were the development of the Meltonfield Seam from a new pit bottom (with diesel locomotives and five ton mine cars), a new pit bottom in the Barnsley Seam (with the introduction of electric trolley locomotives and five ton mine cars) and the renewal of the coal preparation plant. In addition a new 3,700 hp double drum electric winder and housing was installed at the East Pit (upcast shaft) to wind the output from the Meltonfield Seam at a depth of 764 yards.

During the 1960s the colliery was producing an annual output of 1,131,863 tons with a labour force of 1,416 men.

The colliery closed in 1995.

Accidents: None are recorded.

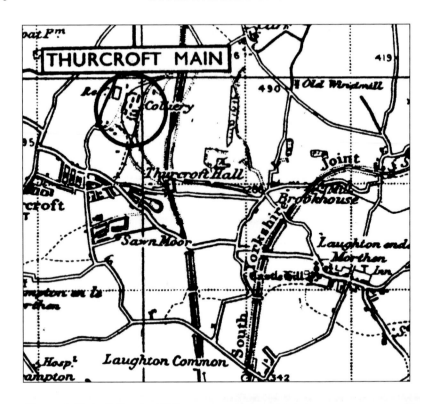

Thurcroft Main Colliery, c.1920.

THURCROFT MAIN COLLIERY

Owners: United Steel Companies Ltd. Treeton, Rotherham, previously owned by Rothervale Collieries Ltd.

Location: Thurcroft near Rotherham.

History: The colliery is situated five miles south-east of Rotherham.

Sunk between 1909 and 1912, the shafts reached a depth of almost 800 yards and intersected three workable seams, the Barnsley, the Parkgate and the Swallow Wood. A major fault of 150 yards displacement encountered in the two shafts resulted in the pit bottom levels being several yards higher than the workings. Inclined drifts had to be used as links to transport men and materials to the coalfaces. The first coal was wound in 1914.

The Barnsley seam was extensively exploited during the early life of the colliery and produced the bulk of coal tonnage until its exhaustion in 1968.

Since 1974 a new coal preparation plant, skip winding and underground staple bunker were installed.

Annual production was around 440,000 tons mainly from the Haigh Moor and Swallow Wood seams with a workforce of 800 men.

The colliery closed in November 1991.

Accidents: None are recorded.

TINSLEY PARK COLLIERY

Owners: Tinsley Park Colliery Co. Ltd.

Location: Tinsley Park.

History: The Tinsley Park Collieries were situated about three miles from the centre of Sheffield.

The first shaft was sunk in 1852 to work the Barnsley and High Hazel seams and produce around 4,000 tons per week of good quality steam and house coal.

Further shafts were sunk in June 1902 to reach the Parkgate seam at a depth of 465 yards and then again in 1909 to the Silkstone seam at a depth of 550 yards. Together they produced a weekly output of 9,000 tons, employing over 2,000 miners. Earl Fitzwilliam retained the royalty rights.

The original Benjamin Huntsman, a Sheffield Quaker and the inventor of cast steel, became associated with Tinsley Colliery in the middle of the eighteenth century prior to the sinking of the first shaft. The colliery remained in the hands of the Huntsman family until 1899 when it was decided to sell the collieries to a limited company so that royalty could be properly developed.

The Sheffield and District Railway put in a branch line to serve the colliery which enabled both Midland and Great Central locomotives to service the Tinsley Park pits. In 1909 the Great Central extended its line from the canal to the pits.

Considerable capital was invested into developing the production of coke by installing thirty-eight new coke ovens and five new steam turbines capable of generating electricity above and below ground.

A new village mining community became established with houses for the workers, an institute and cricket and football grounds.

The colliery was not without its labour problems. In 1869 a strike took place which closed the colliery for nearly two years.

During this period a fire broke out underground which caused considerable damage and the suffocation of two miners whose bodies were not discovered for twenty years.

The colliery closed in 1943.

Accidents: None are recorded.

TREETON COLLIERY

Owners: United Steel Companies Ltd. Treeton, Rotherham.

Location: Treeton.

History: The colliery was originally owned by Rothervale Collieries Ltd. which also owned Orgreave, Fence and Thurcroft Main within the area.

The first sod was cut by Mrs Jaffray, wife of the Chairman of Rothervale Colliery Co. Ltd. on 13 October 1875.

Shafts were sunk in 1877 but before the colliery was at full production it was closed in 1883 due to a recession, but reopened to continue mining coal for the next 100 years. The shafts were deepened in 1936 to 420 yards.

During the period of nationalisation under the National Coal Board and later British Coal Corporation the colliery had many modernisation changes when a 3,282 yard drift connected colliery workings to the surface and a new skip winding unit was installed. During this period 882 men were producing an annual output of 496,224 tons worked from the Wathwood and Swallow Wood seams.

The colliery was connected underground to Orgreave Colliery in the Swallow Wood seam and was sealed in 1981. It was also connected to Thurcroft Colliery in the Barnsley seam which was sealed in 1970.

Coal was transported from Orgreave and Treeton Collieries using the Rothervale locomotives. The coke was transported to the steel works by rail on the Midland Line and the Great Central Line.

The Orgreave coking plant began in 1918 and continued working until 1990. It was a local industry badly hit by the miners' strike in 1984 when the movement of lorries to Scunthorpe attracted the largest number of pickets ever mustered during a dispute in Great Britain. This plant was finally forced to close with Treeton colliery in 1990.

Accidents: None are recorded.

WATH MAIN COLLIERY

Owners: Wath Main Colliery Co. Ltd., Wath-upon-Dearne, Rotherham.

Location: Wath-upon-Dearne.

History: Sunk in 1876 and deepened in 1912 and again in 1923 to a depth of 708 yards.

During the 1960s the colliery was producing 425,529 tons annually from the Newhill and Meltonfield seams with a workforce of 862 men.

The colliery closed in 1986.

Accidents: On 24 February 1930, seven miners were killed in a firedamp explosion ignited by a safety lamp.

CHAPTER ELEVEN

Manpower and Seams Worked Statistics

Many annual records have not survived whilst others only remain incomplete.

It has therefore been necessary to select the years of 1910, 1927, 1945 and 1972 in order to illustrate a wider range of figures over different decades.

Abbreviations:

Underground - U/G

Surface   - Surface

COALFIELDS OF THE BARNSLEY AREA
(Manpower and Coal Seams Statistics)

Colliery	1910		1927		1945		1972		Seams Worked
	U/G	SUR	U/G	SUR	U/G	SUR	U/G	SUR	
Barley Hall	----	----	----	----	----	----	379		Low Fenton
Barrow	2252	576	2060	400	1240	432	1313		Lidgett, Thorncliffe, Parkgate, Silkstone & Swallow Wood
Barnsley Main	979	305	2200	550	365	142	N/A		Thorncliffe, Parkgate, Fenton and Haigh Moor.
Bullcliffe Wood	----	----	2713	412	109	31	297		Top Haigh Moor and Low Haigh Moor
Caphouse	109	61	177	66	138	30	267		Wheatley Lime, Beeston
Darfield Main	731	164	798	213	662	216	875		Dunsil, Melton Field, Parkgate and Beamshaw
Dearne Valley	370	90	430	122	432	126	406		Shafton and Sharlston Top
Denby Grange	453	109	177+	66+	251	59	267		New Hards and Wheatley Lime
Dodworth	1375	276	1060	166	1065	296	1396		Flockton, Parkgate Thorncliffe, Silkstone and Flockton
Emley Moor	660	173	595	210	432	126	267		Blocking, Beeston and New Hards

Colliery	1910 U/G	SUR	1927 U/G	SUR	1945 U/G	SUR	1972 U/G	SUR	Seams Worked
Ferrymoor	----	----	703	126	48	11	347		Shafton
Grimethorpe	2375	467	3300	2192	540	2088			Barnsley, Parkgate Low Beamshaw Melton Field and Fenton
Houghton Main	1634	341	1606	415	1992	464	1540		Barnsley, Top and Low Beamshaw
Monk Bretton	1282	201	695	164	811	227	----		Barnsley, Kents Thick, Beamshaw and Winter
Newmillerdam	----	----	93*	25*	135	35	203		Winter, Beamshaw and Kents Thick
North Gawber	662	176	553	126	747	179	974		Lidgett, Parkgate, Thorncliffe, Silkstone, Barnsley Top and Low Haigh Moor
Park Mill	537	125	585	160	451	162	309		Low Fenton and Flockton
Rockingham	1213	32	560	213	859	251	1453		Harley, Flockton Thick, Low Fenton and Lidgett
Shuttle Eye	167	14	170	21	234	37	222		Beeston and Black Bed
Smithy Wood	480	144	835	144	632	186	447		Thorncliffe, Thin Parkgate, Fenton and Silkstone
South Kirby	1332	201	2394	496	1532	355	1992		Haigh Moor, Flockton, Barnsley Stanley Main, Warren House Barnsley, Beamshaw and Meltonfield
Wentworth Silkstone	----	----	519	82	375	117	489		Parkgate, Flockton, Fenton and Thorncliffe
Woolley	795	206	456+	147+	1948	493	1872		Barnsley, Haigh Moor, Parkgate, Silkstone, Thorncliffe, Lidgett, Low Haigh and Blocking

* 1935 statistics
+ figures include manpower for working multiple seams

COALFIELDS OF THE DONCASTER AREA
(Manpower and Coal Seams Statistics)

Colliery	1910		1927		1945		1972		Seams Worked
	U/G	SUR	U/G	SUR	U/G	SUR	U/G	SUR	
Askern Main	----	----	1206	294	1170	354	1430		Warren House
Bentley	907	303	2954	475	2405	527	1228		Barnsley, Barnsley Deep, Dunsil
Brodsworth Main	1716	395	3580	600	2787	631	2961		Barnsley, Barnsley Deep, Parkgate, Thorncliffe, Dunsil
Frickley	1463	276	3400	2232	518	----			Barnsley, Barnsley Deep, Shafton
Goldthorpe	----	----	276	53	268	80	----		Shafton
Hatfield Main	----	----	1850	300	1987	536	1712		Barnsley, Kents Thick, High Hazel
Hickleton Main	2566	493	2960	650	2825	556	1558		Barnsley, Barnsley Deep, Low Main, Parkgate
Highgate	----	----	148	34	159	66	1340		Shafton
Markham Main	----	----	1909	280	2272	360	1500		Barnsley
Rossington Main	----	----	2000	500	1762	486	1681		Barnsley, Dunsil
South Elmsall	----	----	----	----	124	10	2076		Shafton, Cudworth
Yorkshire Main	182	75	3000	500	2118	474	1783		Barnsley

COALFIELDS OF THE SOUTH YORKSHIRE AREA
(Manpower and Coal Seams Statistics)

Colliery	1910		1927		1945		1970s		Seams Worked
	U/G	SUR	U/G	SUR	U/G	SUR	U/G	SUR	
Aldwarke Main	2331	645	1565	409	1100	246	N/A		Kents Thick, Lidget, Parkgate, Silkstone
Barnburgh	----	----	1766	384	1799	397	1200		Parkgate, Haigh Moor, Newhill, Barnsley and Meltonfield
Brookhouse	----	----	----	----	----	----	757		Thorncliffe
Bullcroft Main	108	97	2713	412	1373	345	N/A		Barnsley, Barnsley Deep
Cadeby Main	2635	660	2087	470	1168	289	1671		Barnsley, Parkgate Beamshaw and Swallow Wood
Car House	228	131	---- (pumping)	----	9 (pumping)	2	N/A		Barnsley, Swallow Wood, Parkgate

Colliery	1910		1927		1945		1970s		Seams Worked
	U/G	**SUR**	**U/G**	**SUR**	**U/G**	**SUR**	**U/G**	**SUR**	
Cortonwood	545	230	1937	601	1540	427	1017		Barnsley, Parkgate, Haigh Moor, Silkstone and Swallow Wood
Denaby Main	1492	522	1480	430	1569	487	N/A		Barnsley, Parkgate
Dinnington	1420	471	1900	520	1103	384	991		Barnsley, Swallow Wood and Haigh Moor
Elsecar Main	644	117	1550	350	1305	472	1206		Parkgate, Haigh Moor, Swallow Wood, Thorncliffe Silkstone
Fence	(ventilating)		35	692	(pumping)		N/A		Barnsley, Swallow Wood, Parkgate
Kilnhurst	2983	622	2884	930	679	202	596		Swallow Wood, Barnsley, Parkgate Silkstone and High Hazel
Kiveton Park	1585	244	1722+	288+	11~6	318	892		Barnsley, Thorncliffe High Hazel and Clowne
Maltby Main	143	196	1650	400	1938	403	1400		Barnsley and Swallow Wood
Manvers Main	2983	622	2884+	930+	1867	682	1545		Barnsley, Parkgate, Melton Field, Haigh Moor Swallow Wood and Silkstone
Mitchell Main	12201	361	1408	392	655	205	N/A		Melton Field, Dunsil, Fenton, Barnsley, Parkgate
Monkton Main	2036	580	3270	809	2936	808	N/A		Winter, Haigh Moor, Top Haigh Moor, Barnsley, Top Softs
New Stubbin	----	----	1450	272	1123	297	853		Barnsley, Parkgate, Thorncliffe, Silkstone
Nunnery	1401	316	697	543	1528	438	N/A		Flockton, Haigh Moor, Parkgate, Silkstone
Orgreave	1644	635	2373+	692+	1230	398	983		Parkgate, Silkstone, Swallow Wood, Flockton
Primrose Hill	359	94	544	177	765	273	N/A		Beeston, Flockton, Silkstone

Colliery	1910		1927		1945		1970s		Seams Worked
	U/G	SUR	U/G	SUR	U/G	SUR	U/G	SUR	
Rotherham Main	960	47	1628	460	261	121	N/A		Barnsley, Swallow Wood, Parkgate, Silkstone, Barnsley Bed
Ridings Drift	N/A		N/A		N/A		227		Shafton
Silverwood	2635	710	3000	875	2306*	617*	1416		Barnsley and Swallow Wood
Thorne	135	172	900	300	1940	520	N/A		High Hazel
Thurcroft Main	55	204	1883	363	1276	283	845		Barnsley, Parkgate, Haigh Moor and Swallow Wood
Tinsley Park	1566	509	1586	416	N/A		N/A		High Hazel, Parkgate, Silkstone Wathwood, Thin Coal, Haigh Moor
Treeton	1276	234	1754	382	951	258	882		Barnsley, Haigh Moor, High Hazel, Wathwood and Swallow Wood
Waleswood	704	237	893	204	527	211	N/A		Flockton, High Hazel, Thorncliffe
Warren House	----	----	----	----		6	N/A		
	(pumping)		(pumping)		(pumping)				
Wath Main	1508	405	1823	546	1501	501	862		Barnsley, Parkgate Haigh Moor and Melton
Wombwell Main	1082	239	1150	250	930	218	N/A		Parkgate, Bramshaw, Bramshaw, Fenton, Thorncliffe, Winter Bed

* Combined with Roundwood Colliery
+ Figures include manpower for working multiple seams

CHAPTER TWELVE

Yorkshire Colliery Companies and Pits During the Early 1900s

Colliery Owner	Address	Name of Mine
Ackton Hall Colliery Co.	Featherstone, Pontefract	Ackworth
Addy & Senior	Cumberworth, Huddersfield	Barncliffe Hill
Ainley, Mrs	Thurgoland, Sheffield	Berry Moor
Allen & Son (Halifax) Ltd.	Halifax	Sunny Vale
Armitage Works Co. Ltd.	Deepcar, Sheffield	Deepcar Henholmes
Askern Coal & Iron Co. Ltd.	Askern, Doncaster	Askern
Aston Coal Co. Ltd.	Swallownest, Sheffield	Aston
Barber, Walker & Co.	Bentley, Doncaster	Bentley
Barnsley Main Colliery Co. Ltd.	Barnsley	Barnsley Main
Barrow Hematite Steel Co. Ltd.	Barnsley	Barrow
Bower, T & RW Ltd.	Woodlesford, Leeds	Allerton Main
Bowling & Co.	Bradford	Toftshaw Bottom
Bramall, C	Oughtibridge, Sheffield	Myers Lane
Briggs & Sons, Jos	Queensbury Colliery, Bradford	Fail Bottom Hole Bottom
Briggs, Son & Co. Ltd.	Whitwood, Normanton	New Market Savile Snydale, Haigh Moor Water Haigh Whitwood, Don Pedro Whitwood, Haigh Moor Whitwood, Silkstone Whitwood, Beeston
Brodsworth Main Colliery Co. Ltd.	Pickburn, Doncaster	Brodsworth Main
Brooke, Abm & Sons Ltd.	Netherton, Wakefield	Netherton
Brooke & Sons, T	Deepcar, Sheffield	Bracken Moor
Brooke Bros.	Shelley, Huddersfield	Greenhouse
Brooke, Geo.	Normanton	Churchfield
Brooke, W	Stocksbridge, Sheffield	Pot House
Brookes Ltd.	Halifax	Walterclough
Brooks & Brooks	Waterloo Main Colliery, Leeds	Waterloo Main
Brown, C	Silkstone Common, Barnsley	Moorend
Brown & Co. Ltd.	Aldwarke, Rotherham	Aldwarke Main Car House, Barnsley Swallow Wood
Brown & Co. Ltd.	Canklow, Rotherham	Rotherham Main
Bullcroft Main Colliery Co. Ltd.	Carcroft, Doncaster	Bullcroft Main
Cardwell, Wm & J	Lepton, Huddersfield	Lepton Edge, Whitley Clough

Colliery Owner	Address	Name of Mine
Carlinghow Colliery Co. Ltd.	Batley	Roche
Carlton Main Colliery Co. Ltd.	Barnsley	Carlton Main
		Frickley
		Grimethorpe
Central Silkstone Collieries Co. Ltd.	Barnsley	Central Silkstone
Chambers Bros	Sheffield	Effingham
Charlesworth, Ltd. J & J	Stanley, Wakefield	Newmarket, Silkstone
Charlesworth, Ltd. J & J	Robin Hood, Wakefield	Robin Hood
Charlesworth, Ltd. J & J	Rothwell Haigh, Leeds	Rothwell Haigh, Fanny Midland
Charlesworth, Ltd. J & J	Kilnhurst, Rotherham	Thrybergh Hall Kilnhurst
Clayton & Speight	Beeston Royds, Leeds	Ravels
Cleckheaton Colliery Co. Ltd.	Cleckheaton	Hunslet Lodge
		Gelderd Road
		Hunsworth Lift
Cortonwood Collieries Co. Ltd.	West Melton, Rotherham	Cortonwood
Crawshaw & Warburton Ltd.	Dewsbury	Chidswell
Crigglestone Collieries Ltd.	Crigglestone, Wakefield	Durkar Crigglestone
Critchley & Sons, Ltd. Jas.	Batley	Batley, West End
Dalton Main Collieries Ltd.	Parkgate, Rotherham	Roundwood, Silverwood
Davies Bros.	Cudworth, Barnsley	Sidcop Main
Dearne Valley Colliery Co. Ltd.	Little Houghton, Barnsley	Dearne Valley
Denaby & Cadeby Main Collieries Ltd.	Denaby Main, Rotherham	Cadeby Main, Denaby Main
Dinnington Main Coal Co. Ltd.	Dinnington, Rotherham	Dinnington
Dyson, J & J	Stannington, Sheffield	Deerpark, Woodend
Elliott, B	Lepton, Huddersfield	Lodge Mill, Throstle Nest
Ellison, Hy	Cleckheaton	Westgate
Farnley Iron Co. Ltd.	Farnley, Leeds	Ashfield, White's
Farnley Iron Co. Ltd.	Colne Bridge, Huddersfield	Helm
Fitzwilliam, Rt. Hon. Earl	Elsecar, Barnsley	Hemingfield, Low Stubbin
Flack, Jos & Son	Scissett, Huddersfield	Upper Bagden
Flockton Coal Co. Ltd.	Horbury, Wakefield	Hartley Bank
Flockton Moor Coal Co.	Flockton, Wakefield	Flockton Moor
Fountain & Burnley Ltd.	Darton, Barnsley	North Gawber, Woolley
Fountain G & Son, Ltd.	Haigh, Barnsley	Haigh, Darton
Fountain & Son, Ltd.	Haigh, Barnsley	Darton
Fox, Samuel & Co. Ltd.	Stocksbridge, Sheffield	Stocksbridge
Fullerton, J S H	Silkstone, Barnsley	Flockton Moor
Fyfe & Co, John P	Shipley, Bradford	Shipley

Colliery Owner	Address	Name of Mine
Garforth Colliery	Garforth, Leeds	Garforth
Garforth, F	Drighlington, Bradford	Spring Gardens
Glass Houghton & Castleford Collieries Ltd.	Castleford	Glass Houghton
Grange Lane Colliery Co.	Grange Lane, Rotherham	Grange Lane
Gregory, Reddish & Co. Ltd.	Deepcar, Sheffield	Clough
Hague, Fred	Rawmarsh, Rotherham	Rawmarsh
Haigh, Joseph	Bruntcliffe, Leeds	Victoria
Haigh Moor Coal Co. Ltd.	Crigglestone, Wakefield	Crigglestone Main
Halliday & Co., G & W	Howcans, Halifax	Howcans
Hawkyard, W	Elland, Halifax	Victoria
Heeley B	New Mill, Huddersfield	Lane End
Hepworth Iron Co. Ltd.	Hazlehead, Sheffield	Sledbrook, Smut Hole
Hickleton Main Colliery Co. Ltd.	Thurnscoe, Rotherham	Hickleton Main
Hinchliffe & Co., J	Penistone	Bullhouse, Crowledge Handbank
Hodroyd Coal Co.	Brierley, Barnsley	Brierley
Holliday & Sons, P	East Ardsley Collieries, Wakefield	East Ardsley
Holliday, W D	Gildersome, Leeds	Hilltop
Holmes Farm Colliery Co.	Bowling, Bradford	Holmes Farm
Horn, John	Cumberworth, Huddersfield	Top O' Hill
Houghton Main Colliery Co. Ltd.	Barnsley	Houghton Main
Howdenclough Collieries Ltd.	Birstall, Leeds	Howdenclough
Howley Park Coal and Cannel Co.	Batley	Howley Park
Hoyland Silkstone Coal & Coke Co.	Barnsley	Hoyland
Ingham's Thornhill Collieries Ltd.	Dewsbury	Combs Ingham
Jackson M, Mrs	Bolsterstone, Sheffield	Holly Bush
Jagger & Co.	Whitley, Dewsbury	How Royd
Jagger & Elliott	Flockton, Wakefield	Grange Ash
Kendal Green Colliery Co. Ltd.	Worsborough Bridge, Barnsley	Kendal Green
Kitson & Sons, J	Denby Dale, Huddersfield	Bank Royd
Kiveton Park Coal Co. Ltd.	Kiveton Park, Sheffield	Kiveton Park
Knowles, W T	Elland, Halifax	Ash Grove
Lawson, Andrew & Sons	Hoyland, Barnsley	Thurstonland
Layden & Hobson	Ringinglow, Sheffield	Ringinglow
Leeds Fireclay Co. Ltd.	Wortley, Leeds	Breakneck, Coronation Elland Road, Greenside, Harehills, Rock, Royds, Shibden Hall, Sunny Bank & Cardigan

Colliery Owner	Address	Name of Mine
Leeds Fireclay Co. Ltd.	Tong, Leeds	Beulah
Leeds Fireclay Co. Ltd.	Fieldhouse, Huddersfield	Fieldhouse, New Peace
Leeds Fireclay Co. Ltd.	Halifax	Beacon, Ellen Royd, Field
Lidgett Colliery Co. Ltd.	Tankersley, Barnsley	Lidgett
Linfit Lane Coal Co.	Huddersfield	St. Helens, Woolrow
Lister-Kaye, F	Denby Grange Collieries, Wakefield	Denby Grange (Caphouse), Prince of Wales
Liversedge Coal Co.	Liversedge	Strawberry Bank
Locke & Co. (Newland) Ltd.	Normanton	St John's, Scale Coal
Lockwood & Elliott	Grange Moor, Wakefield	Shuttle Eye
Lodge, H. Ltd.	Ryhill, Wakefield	Goldthorpe, Ryhill
Lofthouse Colliery Co.	Wakefield	Lofthouse
Longden & Sons, G. Ltd.	Neepsend, Sheffield	Wadsley Park
Longley, Wm.	Lower Cumberworth, Clough House, Huddersfield	Cumberworth
Low Laithes Colliery Co. Ltd.	Ossett, Wakefield	Low Laithes Wrenthorpe
Low Moor Co. Ltd.	Bradford	Chairbarrow, Coates, Drake, Hartshead, High Moor Lane, Rhodes, Scholes, Taylor Mills, Three Nuns, West Field
Low Moor Co. Ltd.	Beeston, Leeds	Beeston
Low Moor Co. Ltd.	Osmondthorpe, Leeds	Osmondthorpe
Lowood J & Co. Ltd.	Deepcar, Sheffield	Wharncliffe
Luty & Sons, F	Elland, Halifax	New Hall
Maltby Main Colliery Co. Ltd.	Chesterfield	Maltby Main
Mann, Abel	Liversedge	Southfield
Mann & Co.	Barnsley	Bankhouse
Manor Haigh Moor Colliery Co.	Wakefield	Manor
Manvers Main Collieries Ltd.	Wath-on-Dearne, Rotherham	Manvers Main
Matthew, John & Sons	Holbeck, Leeds	Low Close
Medley, Jesse	Huddersfield	Brown Royd
Meltham Silica Firebrick Co.	Meltham, Huddersfield	Green End, Royd Edge
Micklefield Coal and Lime Co. Ltd.	Micklefield, Leeds	Ledstone Luck, Peckfield
Middleton Estate Colliery Co. Ltd.	Leeds	Middleton
Mirfield Colliery Co.	Ravensthorpe, Dewsbury	Calder, Dark Lane, Mirfield Moor
Mitchell Main Colliery Co. Ltd.	Barnsley	Darfield Main, Mitchell Main
Monk Bretton Colliery Co. Ltd.	Barnsley	Monk Bretton
Moorhouse, Henry	New Mill, Huddersfield	Carr Wood

Colliery Owner	Address	Name of Mine
Morton, Ltd, Jos.	Siddal, Halifax	Cinder Hills and Quarry, New Mytholme
Mosley & Sons, D	Bradford	Red Hill
Mottram Wood Colliery Co. Ltd.	Barnsley	Mottram Wood
Musgrave, Ltd, H	South Hiendley, Barnsley	South Hiendley
Naylor & Co. Ltd.	Ossett, Wakefield	Pildacre
Naylor Bros.	Denby Dale, Huddersfield	Pinfold
Nethertown Colliery Co.	Drighlington, Bradford	Nethertown
Netherwood & Co.	Adwalton, Bradford	Lane Side
New Ingleton Collieries Ltd.		Richard, Grove, Nellie
New Monckton Collieries Ltd.	Barnsley	Hodroyd, Monckton Main
New Sharlston Collieries Co. Ltd.	Normanton	Sharlston
New Silkstone and Haigh Moor Coal Co. Ltd.	Castleford	Allerton Bywater
Newton, Chambers & Co. Ltd.	Dropping Well, Rotherham	Grange
Newton, Chambers & Co. Ltd.	Thorncliffe, Sheffield	Norfolk and Smithy Wood
Newton, Chambers & Co. Ltd.	Hoyland Common, Barnsley	Rockingham
Newton, Chambers & Co. Ltd.	Thorncliffe, Sheffield	Tankersley, Thorncliffe
North & Pflaurn	Leeds	Green Top, Blue Hill
Northfield Colliery Co. Ltd.	Ossett, Wakefield	Northfield, Longlands
Nortonthorpe Colliery Co. Ltd.	Scissett, Huddersfield	Nortonthorpe
Nunnery Colliery Co. Ltd.	Sheffield	High Hazels, Nunnery Woodthorpe
Old Silkstone Collieries Ltd.	Dodworth, Barnsley	Dodworth, Thorncliffe, Higham, Redbrook, Silkstone Fall, Stanhope
Pease & Partners Ltd	Thorne Colliery, Doncaster	Thorne
Pickford, Holland & Co.	Sheffield	Little Matlock
Pope & Pearson Ltd.	Normanton	West Riding
Primrose Main Colliery Co. Ltd.	Smithies, Barnsley	Primrose Main
Rainsforth Colliery Co.	Thorpe, Rotherham	Rainsforth
Rhodes, John	Pontefract	Prince of Wales
Rotherham Silkstone Collieries Ltd.	Kimberworth, Rotherham	Jordan
Rothervale Collieries Ltd.	Treeton, Rotherham	Orgreave, Fence, Treeton, Thurcroft Main
Round Green Colliery Co. Ltd.	Barnsley	Housley
Royston & Chambers	Swinton, Rotherham	Lewden Bridge
St. Oswald, Rt. Hon. Lord	Nostell, Wakefield	Nostell
Scott, W	Leeds	Rose Hill
Senior Bros.	Barnsley	Housley
Sharratt & Sons	Elland, Halifax	Storth

Colliery Owner	Address	Name of Mine
Shaw & Co. Ltd.	Kirkburton, Huddersfield	Thorncliffe (Green)
Sheffield Coal Co. Ltd.	Sheffield	Birley (East Pit)
		Birley (Beighton Pit)
Siddons, G C	Loxley, Sheffield	Wadsley Common
Silica Fire Brick Co.	Oughtibridge, Sheffield	Beeley Wood, Silica, Stubbin, Wadsley Common
Skinner & Holford Ltd.	Waleswood Collieries, Sheffield	Waleswood
Smith Bros.	Kirkburton, Huddersfield	Linfit Hill
Smith, John	Barnsley	Pogmoor Main
		Dodworth Road
Soothill Wood Colliery Co. Ltd.	Batley	Soothill Wood
South Kirby, Featherstone & Hemsworth Collieries Ltd.	Featherstone, Pontefract	Featherstone Main
South Kirby, Featherstone & Hemsworth Collieries Ltd.	Kinsley, Wakefield	Hemsworth
South Kirby, Featherstone & Hemsworth Collieries Ltd.	South Kirby, Wakefield	South Kirby, Beamshaw
Stanley Coal Co. Ltd.	Liversedge	Primrose Hill, Stanley, Round Hill
Staveley Coal and Iron Co. Ltd.	Edlington, Doncaster	Yorkshire Main
Stocks, M	Halifax	Ford Hill
Strafford Collieries Co. Ltd.	Barnsley	Rob Royd, Strafford
Stringer & Jaggar Ltd.	Emley Moor, Wakefield	Emley, Waterloo
Stringer & Jaggar Ltd.	Clayton West, Huddersfield	Park Mill
Swift & Netherwood	Lepton, Huddersfield	Victoria
Swift, R M	Thurgoland, Sheffield	Cliffe Bridge
Taylor, Alphonso	Darton, Barnsley	Rye Wood
Taylor, C H	Liversedge	Old Hall
Terry, Greaves & Co. Ltd.	Old Roundwood Collieries, Wakefield	Old Roundwood
Tetlow, John & Son, Ltd.	Manchester	Ramsden Wood
Thornton Bros.	Liversedge	Hare Park
Tinker Bros. Ltd.	Hazlehead, Sheffield	Gatehead, Hazlehead
Tinsley Park Colliery Co. Ltd.	Tinsley Park, Sheffield	Tinsley Park
Towler, W & J H	Gildersome, Leeds	Gildersome, Street Lane
Vernon Colliery Co.	Worsborough Common, Barnsley	Vernon
Vernon-Wentworth, Capt. P O	Wentworth Castle, Barnsley	Low Wood
Victoria Coal & Coke Co. Ltd.	Wakefield	Park Hill
Walsworth, J & H	Bradford	Birkenshaw, Crosses
Walker, W	Wakeley Lane	Wakeley Lane
Waterhouse & Son, F J W	Elland, Halifax	Calder
Wath Main Collieries Co. Ltd.	Wath, Rotherham	Wath Main
West Silkstone Colliery Co. Ltd.	Silkstone Common, Barnsley	West Silkstone

Colliery Owner	Address	Name of Mine
Wharncliffe Silkstone Colliery Co. Ltd.	Tankersley, Barnsley	Wharncliffe Silkstone
Wharncliffe Silkstone Colliery Co. Ltd.	Carlton, Barnsley	Wharncliffe Woodmoor and Wharncliffe Haigh Moor
Wheatley & Render	Adwalton, Bradford	Horse Riggs
Wheatley & Sons, H	Hopton, Mirfield	Hopton Mills
Wheldale Coal Co. Ltd.	Castleford	Fryston, Wheldale
Whinmoor Colliery Co. Ltd.	Rotherham	Whinmoor
Whinney Moor Colliery Co.	Wakefield	Whinney Moor
White Lea Colliery Co. Ltd.	Birstall, Leeds	White Lea
Wombwell Main Colliery Co. Ltd.	Barnsley	Wombwell Main
Wood & Son, Isaac	Allerton Colliery, Bradford	Allerton
Wood & Son, Isaac	Thornton, Bradford	Thornton
Wood & Son, Isaac	Allerton, Bradford	Wilsden
Woodhead & Son, W	Farnley, Leeds	Charles, Grove, Philadelphia, Tong No. 1, Newmarket
Wragg, T	Loxley, Sheffield	Worrall Moor
Yorkshire Iron and Coal Co. Ltd.	Leeds	West Ardsley

CHAPTER THIRTEEN

Yorkshire Colliery Accidents and Disasters

Colliery	Date	Cause	Deaths
Allerton Bywater	10 Mar 1930	Explosion, firedamp, shot-firing	5
Altofts	2 Oct 1886	Explosion, coal dust, shot-firing	20
Barnburgh	24 Apr 1942	Floor upheaval	4
Barnburgh Main	25 Jun 1957	Explosion, firedamp, flash from damaged electric cable	6
Barnsley Main	16-17 Feb 1942	Explosion, firedamp, flash from coal cutter trailing cable	13
Barnsley Main	7 May 1947	Explosion, firedamp, arcing from trailing cable and moving rocker	9
Barrow	15 Nov 1907	Shaft accident, cage collided with girders	7
Bentley	20 Nov 1931	Explosion, firedamp, gob fire or safety lamp	45
Birley Fast Pit	23 Feb 1924	Explosion, firedamp, shot-firing	4
Brookhouse	4 Mar 1958	Shaft accident, excessive speed winding	36
Cadeby Main	9 Jul 1912	2 explosions, firedamp and coal dust gob-fire	88
Car House	16 Jun 1913	Inrush of water	8
Cortonwood	19 Jun 1961	Suffocation from outburst of firedamp caused by floor upheaval	4
Crigglestone	29 Jul 1941	Explosion, firedamp, shot-firing	22
Edmunds Main	8 Dec 1862	Explosion, firedamp, shot-firing	59
Elsecar	22 Dec 1852	Explosion, firedamp, naked light	10
Hartley Bank	23 May 1924	Explosion, firedamp, ignited at switch box of coal cutter	4
Higham	15 Feb 1860	Explosion, firedamp, lighted candle	13
Houghton Main	12 Dec 1930	Explosion, firedamp, shot-firing	7
Ingham	9 Sep 1947	Explosion, firedamp, coal dust spark from flame of safety lamp	12
Lofthouse	21 Mar 1973	Inrush of water	7
Lundhill	19 Feb 1857	Explosion, firedamp	189
Maltby Main	28 Jul 1923	Explosion, firedamp, spontaneous combustion	27
Manvers Main	4 Mar 1945	Explosion, firedamp, ignition caused by damaged trailing cable	5

Colliery	Date	Cause	Deaths
Micklefield	30 Apr 1896	Explosion, firedamp, coal dust	62
Morley	7 Oct 1872	Explosion, firedamp, naked light	34
North Gawber (Lidgett)	12 Sep 1935	Explosion, firedamp, shot-firing	19
Nunnery	3 Dec 1923	Underground haulage accident caused by breakage of haulage rope	7
Oaks	12 Dec 1866	Explosion, firedamp, blown out shot	361
Prince of Wales	1918	Winding accident, cage struck shaft	4
Ravenslodge	4 Aug 1892	Flooding	6
Rawmarsh	20 Nov 1874	Explosion, firedamp, shot-firing	23
St Johns	26 Sep 1959	Explosion, firedamp caused by spark from plug and socket of drilling machine	3
Stanley	4 Mar 1879	Explosion, firedamp caused by naked light	21
Swaithe Main	16 Dec 1875	Explosion, firedamp, shot-firing	143
Thorne	15 Mar 1926	Shaft accident, breakage of capstan engine	6
Thornhill	4 Jul 1893	Explosion, firedamp caused by naked light	139
Victoria	14 Mar 1879	Shaft accident, collision of cages	9
Walton	22 Apr 1959	Explosion, firedamp caused by electric arc from damaged trailing cable	5
Warren Vale	20 Dec 1851	Explosion, firedamp caused by naked light	52
Wath Main	24 Feb 1930	Explosion, firedamp ignited by safety lamp	7
Wharncliffe Carlton	18 Oct 1883	Explosion, firedamp caused by safety lamp	20
Wharncliffe Silkstone	30 May 1914	Explosion, firedamp caused by faulty electric equipment on coal-cutting machine	11
Wharncliffe Woodmoor	6 Aug 1936	Explosion, firedamp caused by sparking at switch or commutator of the loader motor	58
Wheldale	22 Feb 1923	Explosion, firedamp, shot-firing	9

Addendum

It is not my intention to go into the complexities of the coal mining industry or to apportion the blame or causes to any particular government, corporation or trade union for the decline in the industry.

Smoke free zones, nuclear power stations, financial restraints, production costs, market forces, inflation, the deterioration of miners' wages followed by strikes are all ingredients adding to a progressive decline, which has taken place since a period of post war nationalisation success from 1947 to the 1970s.

The result was that during the 1980s until 1995, when the British Coal Corporation (previously the National Coal Board) became denationalised, collieries rapidly ceased production and closed down. In 1994 only nineteen collieries continued producing coal in the entire United Kingdom. Eleven of them were in Yorkshire.

At the time of nationalisation in 1947, no less than 147 National Coal Board collieries were in full production in Yorkshire, but now, as we enter the twenty-first century, this figure is down to six pits; those of the Selby coalfield, of which only Ricall, Stillingfleet and Wistow are still in production (North Selby and Whitemoor closed down), surfacing at Gascoigne Wood, and pits at Maltby Main and Prince of Wales. Yorkshire can still claim to have the largest proportion of collieries remaining in the United Kingdom.

Yorkshire still continues to be the home of the National Coal Mining Museum, at Caphouse Colliery, and Elsecar Heritage Park, a living record of our mining history for future generations to appreciate.

Since this book was written, R J B Mining has been taken over by UK Coal in 2001.

Bibliography

Clayton, Arthur K, *The Newcomen-type Engine at Elsecar, Aspects of Barnsley 3*, Pen & Sword Books Ltd.

Colliery Year Book and Trade Directory, 1927.

Custer, Roger, *The Dearne and Dove Canal, Aspects of Barnsley 3*, Pen & Sword Books Ltd.

Ellis, Norman, *South Yorkshire Collieries. Reflections of a Bygone Age, 1995.*

Glister, B, *Conception and Construction of the Barnsley Canal.* Pen & Sword Books Ltd.

Goodchild, John, *Coals from Barnsley.* Wakefield Historical Publications, 1986.

Guide to the Coalfields 1948, Colliery Guardian.

Hall, Geoffrey *Joseph Beaumont Mining Steward 1792-1847, Aspects of Barnsley 4*, Pen & Sword Books Ltd.

Jones, M and J, *Child Labour in Mines.*

Lake, Fiona and Preece, Rosemary, *Voices From The Dark.* Yorkshire Mining Museum Publications, 1992.

Lodge, Trevor, *Coal for Commerce: Sustaining a Manufacturing Economy, Aspects of Rotherham 3*, Pen & Sword Books Ltd.

Lodge, Trevor, *Midland Railway Branch in South Yorkshire*, Pen & Sword Books Ltd.

Medlicott, Ian P, *Coal Mining on the Wentworth Estate, Aspects of Rotherham 3*, Pen & Sword Books Ltd.

Ministry of Fuel and Power List of Mines, 1945.

National Coal Board - Various leaflets and unmarked papers.

Pickering's List of Mines, 1910.

Index